CREATE!

Food Technology

Barbara Mottershead
Lesley Woods

Series editor
Jenny Jupe

Heinemann

Inspiring generations

Heinemann Educational Publishers
Halley Court, Jordan Hill, Oxford OX2 8EJ
Part of Harcourt Education

Heinemann is the registered trademark of
Harcourt Education Limited

© Barbara Mottershead and Lesley Woods, 2003

First published 2003

07 06 05 04
10 9 8 7 6 5 4 3 2

British Library Cataloguing in Publication Data is
available from the British Library
on request.

ISBN 0 435 41218 3

Produced and illustrated by Hardlines Ltd,
Charlbury, Oxford

Original illustrations © Harcourt Education
Limited 2003

Cover illustration by Matt Buckley

Printed in Italy by Printer Trento S.r.l.

Acknowledgements
The publishers would like to thank the following
for permission to use copyright material: McVitie's
Jaffa Cakes pack used by consent of United Biscuits
(UK) Limited, p. 77; Quorn™ (a trademark of
Marlow Foods), pp. 58 and 66.

The publishers would like to thank the following
to use photographs: Alamy, p. 90; Alessi, p. 63 (top
right); Anthony Blake Picture Library, p. 36
(bottom); BBC Stills, p. 63 (top and bottom left);
Corbis, pp. 62, 83 (left), 89; Cornish Picture
Library, p. 27 (right); Haddon Davies, pp. 7, 9, 14,
16, 17, 20, 21 (bottom), 34 (right), 36 (top left and
right), 40, 45, 47 (right), 55, 56, 65 (bottom left), 72
(right), 74, 81, 84, 91; Duerrs, p. 83 (middle);
EatmeSoftware.com, p. 83 (right); Foodpix, p. 72
(left); Farmhouse Biscuits, pp. 78, 79 (top right,
bottom left and right); Getty, pp. 6, 34 (left); Linda
Haisley, 'Cakes for all occasions', 7 Newland Mill,
Witney, Oxon, OX28 3HH; Marks and Spencer, p.
26 (top); PA News, p. 63 (right); Roger Scruton,
pp. 19, 26 (bottom left and right), 27, 38, 39, 46, 47
(left), 51, 79 (top left); Warburtons, p. 86.

Every effort has been made to contact copyright
holders of material reproduced in this book. Any
omissions will be rectified in subsequent printings
if notice is given to the publishers.

There are links to relevant websites in this book.
In order to ensure that the links are up-to-date,
that the links work and that the sites are not
inadvertently linked to sites that could be
considered offensive, we have made the links
available on the Heinemann website at
www.heinemann.co.uk/hotlinks. When you access
this site, the express code for this book is 2183P.

Key Stage 3 Strategy links
The following logos are used throughout this book
to highlight different Key Stage 3 Strategy links.

(DMA) Design and Make Assignment

(D) Designing

(FPT) Focused Practical Task

(ICT) ICT

(ABC) Literacy

(123) Numeracy

(PA) Product analysis

(TS) Thinking skills

Tel: 01865 888058   www.heinemann.co.uk

Contents

What is Food Technology?

Objectives

In this lesson you will:

- recap your understanding of what Food Technology is
- reinforce the basic hygiene expectations in the food room.

Key words

product analysis	finding out about a food product by looking at it, reading the packaging, taking the product apart and tasting it
modelling	developing and trying out new ideas
hygiene	cleanliness, keeping clean to avoid food poisoning

Do you remember what Food Technology is? It is using knowledge and skills to design and make good-quality food products to meet consumer needs. Some of you will have carried out Food Technology tasks in your primary school. You might have learned how to make bread and then design special bread.

Think about it!

Pair up with the person next to you, or with a person who didn't go to your primary school, and discuss with them all the Food Technology tasks you can remember doing in primary school. Make a list to compare with the others in your class.

A *Tasting is not grabbing the biggest piece*

B *Tasting is a scientific process*

Below is a list of the different things you will do to progress in Food Technology.

- Tasting is not grabbing the biggest piece, eating it and saying, 'That was nice'! Tasting is a scientific process that helps you to make decisions about a food product.
- **Product analysis** is not prodding, touching and saying, 'I don't like that'. Product analysis is looking at a product in detail and working out what you can learn from it.

C *Researching your product will make it more successful in the end*

- Research means finding information and learning new things to help you make successful food products. You need to know what you want to find out and why this will help you. For example, if you want to make a vegetable sauce to serve with pasta you won't look at recipes for chocolate desserts, but you will look at vegetable and Italian recipe books and find out which vegetables people prefer and which variety of vegetable sauces supermarkets sell.

grated

sliced

chipped

D *Investigating different methods of preparing a potato*

Experimenting and investigating is not putting lots of ingredients together and seeing what happens. Nor is it cutting up ingredients to look at what is inside them. Experimenting and investigating is part of research and is really about **modelling** with ingredients. It is about trying out different kinds of an ingredient, for example, discovering what shaped pasta is best with a runny sauce. It is also about trying out different sizes, shapes or quantities of ingredients, for example, what sort of chocolate makes the best chocolate cookie – grated chocolate, chocolate chips or cut up chunks of chocolate?

Learning how to make successful food products uses different knowledge and skills, such as choosing suitable equipment, **hygiene**, and following written instructions.

Evaluating is not saying, 'I like that cake, I'll make it again'. Evaluating is thinking about how successful your food product is and how you could improve it.

These things are all important in Food Technology. There's plenty to find out and learn. Have fun!

Hygiene

You already know that following good hygiene rules is common sense. None of us wants to become ill, so we follow certain procedures before we handle food. We followed certain hygiene rules in primary school when we worked with food and we follow them in our kitchen at home.

Before you work with food you must:

- wash your hands
- put on an apron
- wipe clean the surface you are going to work on, preferably with antibacterial cleaner. When you have finished working with food you must wash up your equipment in hot soapy water.

Food storage

Correct storage of ingredients and food products is an important part of hygiene. What sorts of ingredients need to be stored in the refrigerator?

At home some foods are put in the refrigerator:

- to keep cold
- to make them last longer
- to slow down the growth of bacteria.

Think about it!

1 Which of the foods in **E** match the three different reasons given for storing food in a fridge?

2 Look around your food room and make sure you know where the refrigerators are.

3 Read this list of pizza ingredients. You arrive in school with these ingredients at 9 a.m. and your Food Technology lesson is not until 2 p.m.

> **QUICK PIZZA**
>
> 1 pizza base
> tube of tomato puree
> 100g cheese
> tin of pineapple
> 4 slices ham
> 1 red pepper

a) **ABC** Write down a list of the ingredients that must be stored in a fridge.

b) Which ingredients could be stored in a fridge?

c) If your Food Technology lesson was at 11 a.m. where would you store the finished pizza after it had cooled down? Why?

Plenary

Did you remember many of the rules to follow in Food Technology? Now apply them during practical activities and when storing ingredients.

Learning more about products

Evaluating food products

Food Technology is about designing and making food products to meet consumer needs. Information about consumers' needs can be gained by evaluating existing products similar to the ones you are about to design and make.

In the food industry, product analysis is carried out before the designing of new products. The design team want to learn about products other companies have made.

They will investigate:

- what they look like
- how much there is
- how much they cost
- what they taste like.

A *Product analysis in the food industry*

Once you have learned as much as you can about a food product by looking at it, measuring it, weighing it and disassembling it, you need to taste it! This is called sensory testing or **sensory analysis**.

What is your ideal product?

But wait! You will learn more if you first of all think about your ideal product. For example, when you eat a scone, what do you like it to taste, look and smell like? You need to use technical words (adjectives) that accurately describe your ideal products. Think about the last apple you ate and choose four adjectives to describe it. You will probably use 'crunchy' and 'juicy' as two of the words. Now think about a scone. Think in your head what a scone should be like. You can think about colour and size as well as texture and taste. These words might help you: 'crumbly', 'quite sweet', 'thick', 'shiny', 'golden brown'. Try adding other words.

Sometimes it is easier to think about what a product should not be like first. A scone shouldn't be 'flat' like a biscuit, it shouldn't be 'chewy' or look 'dull'. What other adjectives can you use to describe what it shouldn't be like?

The food industry use attribute profiles during tasting sessions. **Attribute profiles** are a visual way to interpret a food product. An example of an attribute profile for a sweet scone is set out in **B**.

B

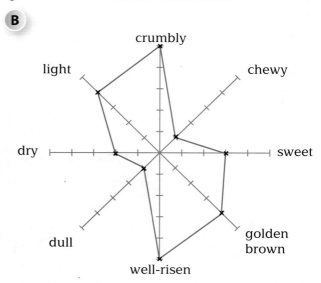

Image **B** shows an ideal attribute profile for a scone. You could draw your own. It might not be the same as **B**, for example, you might want it sweeter or slightly chewy.

Tasting

At last it is time to taste but before you eat anything you must:

- wash your hands
- collect a glass of water (so you do not mix flavours up in your mouth when you eat more than one kind of product)
- have a tasting record sheet in front of you.

Fill in your record sheet and write a brief evaluation explaining what you have learned from this tasting. Your record sheet might look like the one in **C**.

Now you have completed a product analysis you can decide what you would like your scone to be like when you make it. You can draw an ideal attribute profile and you can draw a picture of what you want it to look like. Include exact sizes. You could include extra ingredients you want to add to a basic recipe. Finally, decide how you will **glaze** it.

C

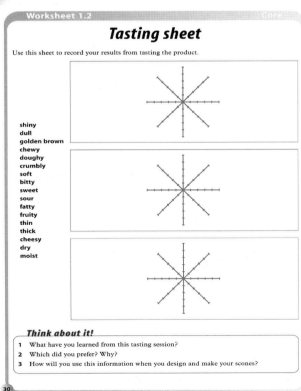

Worksheet 1.2   Core

Tasting sheet

Use this sheet to record your results from tasting the product.

shiny
dull
golden brown
chewy
doughy
crumbly
soft
bitty
sweet
sour
fatty
fruity
thin
thick
cheesy
dry
moist

Think about it!

1 What have you learned from this tasting session?
2 Which did you prefer? Why?
3 How will you use this information when you design and make your scones?

30

Think about it!

1 (123) Look at the two different scones in photo **D**.

D

a) Compare their shape and size and comment on their appearance. Has a glaze been used to produce a good finish?

b) If possible, weigh each scone.

c) Measure the height and radius.

d) Disassemble each one to find out the ratio of fruit to scone mixture.

e) What have you learned from this?

2 (ABC) Now look at the scone packaging in **E**.

E

10 SULTANA SCONES
Ingredients Wheat Flour, Partially Reconstituted Whey Powder, Sugar, Vegetable Oil and Hydrogenated Vegetable Oil, Sultanas (7%), Raising Agents (Disodium Diphosphate, Sodium Bicarbonate), Salt, Preservative (Potassium Sorbate).
Suitable for Vegetarians
Suitable for Home Freezing: Freeze on day of purchase.
To defrost: Defrost thoroughly in a cool place for two hours.
Storage instructions: Store in a cool dry place and once opened in an airtight container.

a) Look at the list of ingredients. Are there ingredients you have not heard of before? What else can you learn from the list?

b) What other information can you learn from the packaging?

(TS) c) What is the packaging in the picture made from? Is there more than one material used? Why? Do they have different functions?

Plenary

Now you should be able to evaluate any food product using the skills you have learned.

Using equipment

Objectives

In this lesson you will:
- learn about new equipment
- find out how to weigh and measure ingredients.

Key words

metric	measurements in grams, kilos, millilitres and litres
imperial	measurements in ounces, pounds, fluid ounces and pints

Look around the food room. Do you know where everything is? Do you know where the equipment is stored? What does it do?

In primary school, special equipment may have been brought in for you to use in Food Technology lessons. It may be a new experience for you to work in a specialist food room.

Some equipment is dangerous

Sharp knives have to be carried safely, that is, held by the handle with the blade pointing to the floor. Knives should always be used with a chopping board, and the hand holding the food should be shaped like a claw (see **A**).

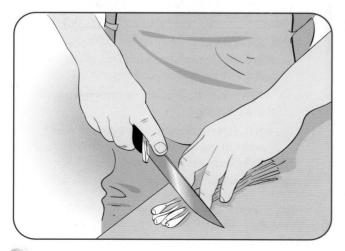

A Cutting safely

Electrical equipment must be plugged in so that the lead is not near water and so no one can trip up over it. You should have instructions on how to use the equipment and the power must be turned off after use.

Working it out

If you read a recipe you can usually work out what equipment you might need. Look at the scone recipe in **B** and decide what equipment you will need.

B

Scone recipe

Ingredients

200g self raising flour

50g margarine

125ml milk

Method

1. Check oven is on at 220°C or Gas Mark 6.

2. **Sieve** flour into a **mixing bowl** and add margarine. Cut up the margarine with a **knife** and then 'rub in' with your fingertips.

3. Add nearly all the milk at once **measuring jug**. Mix with a knife and then your hands until it fis a soft dough.

4. Lightly pat dough on a floured surface until 2cm thick. Cut into shapes with a **biscuit cutter**.

5. Grease a **baking tray** and place scones on it. Glaze the scones with the remaining milk **pastry brush**.

6. Bake for 10–15 minutes.

7. Remove scones from the oven when golden brown. Cool on a **cooling rack**.

C

Photo **C** shows the equipment you need to collect at the beginning of the practical task.

Other equipment

D shows some other useful pieces of equipment.

Colander: to drain the water from pasta, potatoes and rice, or to wash fruit and vegetables.

Whisk: to stop lumps forming in sauces, or to add air to a mixture such as an omelette.

Spatula: to scrape out all mixture from a bowl.

Food slice: to turn over food in a frying pan.

Rolling pin: to flatten biscuit mixture and pastry so it is thin.

Vegetable peeler: an easier way to peel vegetables; safer than using a knife.

D

Measuring and weighing

The last thing you need to learn before your practical task is how to read measurements on a recipe and then how to accurately measure out the ingredients.

You should use **metric** measurements (grams, kilos, millilitres and litres) but you might be used to using **imperial** measurements at home (ounces, pounds, fluid ounces and pints). **E** is a quick conversion table.

25 grams =	1 ounce
400 grams =	1 pound
1 kilogram =	2 pounds and 8 ounces
50 millilitres =	$\frac{1}{4}$ pint and 5 fluid ounces
300 millilitres =	$\frac{1}{2}$ pint and 10 fluid ounces
1 litre =	1 pint and 12 fluid ounces

E   *Metric to imperial measurements conversion table*

There is another way to measure small quantities: spoons!

There are three kinds of spoons that we could use – teaspoon, dessertspoon and tablespoon – but only two are used in recipes.

A level tablespoon is the same as a heaped dessertspoon, and a heaped teaspoon is the same as a level dessertspoon, which is why a dessertspoon is not used for measuring.

Think about it!

ABC It is also very important to know the abbreviations of different measures in recipes. Find out what these abbreviations mean:

g.	kg.	tbsp.	l.	oz.
lb.	ml.	fl.oz.	tsp.	pt.

Imagine if you mixed up your tsp with your tbsp when you were adding salt to a recipe!

Plenary

Now you are ready to complete your practical task. You will use the knowledge and skills you have learned at primary school and those you have learned in the last few lessons. You will build on this knowledge and skill over the next three years.

The balanced plate

What is healthy eating? Do you need to eat healthily? Yes, you do. Healthy eating can be as simple as choosing to eat one portion of chips per week rather than two portions of chips a day. It is about changing the types of foods we eat – eating fruit instead of chocolate, drinking water instead of sweet, fizzy drinks. Look at the balanced plate in **A**.

When making a choice about food it is important to consider the balanced plate and the **properties** of **ingredients**. We can divide these properties into three groups.

● Nutritional properties – ingredients that make sure you have a **balanced diet**, for example, using low-fat products and eating more vegetables.

● Functional properties – ingredients that thicken foods, make foods shine and bind things together.

● Sensory properties – ingredients that add flavour, texture or aroma to foods, or that improve the appearance of food by adding colour, for example.

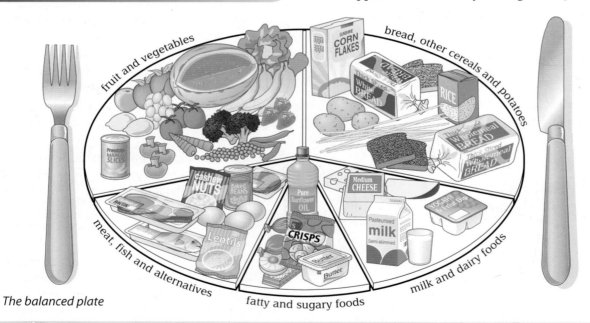

A The balanced plate

Let us look at the example in **B** of the typical meals and snacks that a twelve-year-old boy or girl may eat during one day.

Breakfast	Lunch	Tea/dinner
Chocolate-coated cereal with milk	A cheese sandwich on white bread and butter

A bottle of cola

A blueberry muffin | Burger and chips
Apple turnover |

Snacks during the day

Three bags of crisps

One chocolate bar

A hot chocolate drink

Two biscuits

Two cans of fizzy orange

B   *Food for a day*

C shows how these meals and snacks fit into the balanced plate.

C

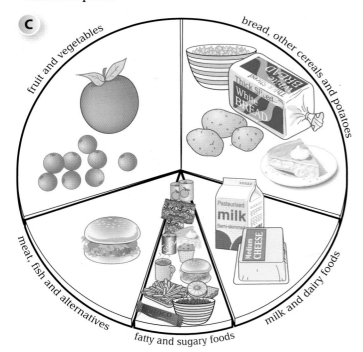

fruit and vegetables

bread, other cereals and potatoes

meat, fish and alternatives

fatty and sugary foods

milk and dairy foods

Think about it!

1   Look at the Factfile. Make one suggestion for each of the things that are recommended to achieve healthy eating.

2   **ABC** There is quite a lot wrong with the meals and snacks in **B**. What could be changed to make it a healthier day's eating?

3   Look at the ideas in **D**. Can you suggest others? Discuss this with the person next to you and come up with some more ideas for healthier eating.

Change some of the snacks for fresh fruit	Drink more water instead of fizzy drinks
Grill the burger	Add salad to the sandwich
Change white bread for wholemeal bread	Add baked beans to tea/dinner and change chips to baked potato

D   *Ways to make the meals and snacks in **B** healthier*

4   **ABC** Now think about what you usually eat during the day.

   a) Write down all the foods you have eaten today. Put the foods into the correct section of a balanced plate outline.

   b) Now suggest ways in which you could change foods to make your daily diet more balanced.

5   Ask your neighbour/grandparent/teenage relation/parent about their daily intake of foods. Record your findings and then work out how to make it more balanced.

6   Describe how fruits and vegetables contribute to getting the dietary balance correct.

7   Salt brings out the flavour in foods. However, too much salt is thought to be unhealthy. What other ingredients could be used instead of salt?

Plenary

Use this information to check out the foods you are eating every day. You could also check out the food products you make in Food Technology. Make sure they are balanced and include enough starch, fruits and vegetables.

Vegetables

Objectives

In this lesson you will:

- find out about vegetables and where they come from
- explore the differences between raw and cooked vegetables
- gain practical experience of food preparation
- investigate the functional properties of soup
- investigate the ingredients for soup.

Key words

texture what foods feel like in your mouth

functional properties characteristics of ingredients that can be used to produce particular types of mixtures and food products

Vegetables fit into the healthy eating idea very well. We are recommended to eat five portions of fruit and vegetables each day. Vegetables grow above and below the ground. These can be grouped into:

- stems
- roots
- bulbs
- leaves
- flowers
- tubers
- pulses
- fruit vegetables.

Type of vegetable	Example	Type of vegetable	Example
Stem	Celery	Roots	Carrot
Bulbs	Onion	Tubers	
Fruit vegetables		Leaves	Cabbage
Flowers		Pulses	Peas

A Grouping vegetables

Tasting and testing

Different vegetables have different tastes, **textures** (what they feel like in your mouth), looks and colours and many change dramatically when cooked.

Think about it!

1   Draw your own table like the one in **B** and fill it in with as many names of different types of vegetables as you can. Some examples have been provided.

2   Find out more about one of the facts listed in the Factfile.

3   **ABC** Write a report about four different vegetables from different groups listed in **B**. Describe the functional, sensory and nutritional properties you think they have.

4   **TS** Find out how and where potatoes, carrots and cauliflower should be stored. What would happen to them if they were incorrectly stored?

FPT Vegetables

Examine the vegetables you have been given, some are raw and some are cooked. Look at each carefully and use the worksheet to record your findings.

Factfile

- Nowadays you can buy strawberries all year round because they are imported from warmer climates. In Britain they only grow in the summer.
- Baby vegetables are popular. Why?
- Frozen vegetables can be as healthy as fresh ones.
- Farmers in less developed countries can be exploited to provide us with cheap food.
- Green beans may travel thousands of air miles before they reach our supermarket shelves

Soup

Soup is a great way to use many vegetables to make a quick nutritious meal or snack. It is easy to choose different vegetables to put into this product. There are so many varieties of soup in the shops, for example, lentil and bacon, spicy Mediterranean, Scotch broth or carrot and coriander.

Soup, and other food products, often contain a combination of ingredients. Each of these ingredients does a different job in the product. In soup there are ingredients to flavour, colour and thicken the soup. There also have to be ingredients to provide texture and supply the liquid. These are called **functional properties**.

Think about it!

1   🖥 Use different research techniques to describe as many different ways as you can of serving and eating potatoes. You could do research on the Internet or in recipe books. You could talk to other people as well as your using own knowledge

2   Table **B** shows some ingredients that have different functions in soup. Fill in the blank spaces with other ingredients.

Colour	Flavour/ seasoning	Texture	Liquid	Thickening
Carrots	Leeks	Mushrooms	Vegetable stock	Flour
	Salt			
	Carrots	Yams	Tomato juice	Yams

B   *The functions of ingredients in soup*

3   In **C** there is a label from a can of soup. Identify the ingredients which colour, flavour, thicken and season the soup.

4   Investigate and explain how you could make sure that a particular soup had the following outcomes:

   ● a smooth consistency

   ● ingredients of a similar size, for example in minestrone.

5   Soup may be bought in many ways – tinned, dried, fresh chilled. Find out the differences between these types of soup and record your findings.

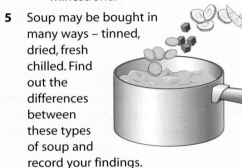

 C

Royal Game Soup

Baxters Soups are special because of the quality and taste we put into them. We use the best and freshest ingredients in our family recipes for your enjoyment. This recipe is based on the first soup created by Baxters in 1929. This delicious hearty soup is made from venison in a rich tasty stock.

Audrey Baxter.

INGREDIENTS
Highland Water, Game (4%) (Venison, Pheasant), Potato, Carrot, Rusks, Onion, Swede, Venison Liver, Wheatflour, Modified Cornflour, Salt, Venison Heart, Yeast Extract, Sugar, Colour (Ammonia Caramel), Pepper, Spice Extracts. Total Meat Content 6%.

NUTRITION INFORMATION		
Typical values Per 100g		*Per ½ can serving*
ENERGY 124kJ/30kcal		256kJ/60kcal
PROTEIN	2.1g	4.4g
CARBOHYDRATE	4.3g	8.9g
(of which sugars)	(0.8g)	(1.7g)
FAT	0.4g	0.8g
(of which saturates)	(0.1g)	(0.2g)
FIBRE	0.2g	0.4g
SODIUM	0.5g	1.0g

DUE TO THE METHODS USED IN THE MANUFACTURE OF THIS PRODUCT, IT MAY CONTAIN NUT TRACES.

COOKING INSTRUCTIONS: CONVENTIONAL - Empty contents into a saucepan and heat gently, stirring occasionally. Do not boil. MICROWAVE - Empty contents into a non - metallic food container. Cover and microwave on full power for 3 minutes, stir the soup, then heat for a further 1 - 2 minutes (Based on a 650 watt microwave oven).

If you would like further information about our other fine foods or if you are not entirely satisfied, please write, quoting the code from the can end. Baxters of Speyside Ltd, Fochabers, Moray, Scotland IV32 7LD. www.baxters.com

STEEL   UK MCO EEC

net 415 g

BEST BEFORE EN
SEE CAN END

IF YOU WOULD PRE
TO OPEN WITH A C
OPENER, JUST TU
THE CAN UPSIDE D

🍲 Let's make some soup

D   This focused practical task is to make some soup. You will either follow a recipe you have been given or perhaps decide on the ingredients yourself.

1   Making the soup involves a number of processes to prepare the ingredients. List these processes and describe why you chose them for each particular ingredient.

2   After making the soup, describe its appearance and flavour. If you were to make it again, what changes would you make? Why and how would you make these changes?

Plenary

This information has started you thinking about which parts of plants vegetables are from. You have also looked at grouping ingredients according to their function (what they do).

You have made soup and considered the functions of the ingredients you chose

Varieties of vegetables and fruit

Objectives

In this lesson you will:

- learn that there are different varieties of vegetable
- investigate and use different types of fresh and processed vegetables
- use fruits as part of the balanced plate
- gain practical experience in the preparation of fruit.

Key words

preservation	treating food to make it last longer, for example, by freezing, adding sugar or acid, or drying
processed food	food that has been changed in some way from its original state, for example, cheese, flour, tomatoes, corned beef and ready-prepared meals
design specification	information about what kind of product you should make
criteria	rules or targets against which a product is checked

There are lots of tomatoes available in the shops but how do you know which sort is best for your purpose? It depends on what use the tomato will have – for a salad, for cooking, as a garnish? Look at the varieties in **A** and suggest a use for each.

Processing food

The choice is made greater by foods being processed in different ways. Sometimes the processing preserves

A *There are many varieties of tomatoes*

B *There are many types of processed tomatoes available*

the food, which means it has a longer shelf life (lasts longer). Preservation can make **processed food** look and taste different although it came from the same source as the unprocessed food. Here are some examples of ways that tomatoes can be processed.

Think about it!

1. Look at potatoes, carrots and sweetcorn in the same way as we have looked at tomatoes. Collect and display pictures and information about the different types of processing of these foods.

2. After carrying out some research in recipe or information books, write down all the ways you have found the following types of tomatoes could be used in food products:
   - dried
   - juice
   - canned
   - fresh.
   - paste/puree

3. **ICT** Using genetically modified foods concern some people. Find out what genetically modified tomatoes are and why they are grown.

4. Many vegetables are frozen to make them last longer. Find out whether fresh or frozen vegetables are better for us. Explain your reasons.

FPT A basic pizza

D Making a pizza can involve the use of tomatoes in all kinds of ways. Look closely at them as you are preparing and using them.

1. Don't forget to plan out the production of the pizza before you begin.

2. Record all the different ways you have used tomatoes on your pizza.

Fruit

Fruit is an important part of our daily diet. You can eat it as it is or in a fruit salad, or you can drink it as a fruit drink. Fruit provides us with vitamin C, which is important for healthy skin, healthy gums and to help wounds heal quickly. Fruit also provides fibre.

Making a fruit salad

Decide what type of salad you want – crunchy, soft or multi-coloured? This will be the **design specification**; it lists the **criteria** for a food product such as colour, texture, and flavour. It is what you want your product to be like. The specification will help you to evaluate and develop your ideas.

FPT A simple fruit salad

D Choose four or five fruits. Peel (if you need to) and slice or chop. Add a little fresh fruit juice and it's ready to eat! Describe the salad's appearance and flavour and if it matches your design specification. If you made the fruit salad again would you change anything - what and why?

FPT Easy fruit smoothie

D Take two or three soft fruits (one should be a banana), wash, peel (if you need to) and chop roughly. Put into a blender with 100ml milk and blend! Describe what your drink looked and tasted like.

Plenary

You should now understand where vegetables come from and the different groups and varieties of vegetables that are available. You have also looked at their functional properties and how vegetables can be processed. You have used vegetables in FTPs. You should also be able to write a design specification for a food product and make products containing different fruits.

Think about it!

List all the fruits you recognize in **C**. Think of their flavours and textures and put them in a table similar to the one in **D**. Some may fit in more than one section.

D

Crunchy	Soft	Sweet	Watery	Hard
Apple		Apple		

C

Salads

Objectives

In this lesson you will:

- evaluate ready-prepared salads by tasting and testing
- experiment with preparing salad ingredients including ratios
- introduce salad dressings.

Key words

emulsification the process by which ingredients that do not mix are stabilized, for example, egg is used to stablilize oil and water in mayonnaise

Look at **A**. Is it a salad? It is what most people think of as a salad. But **A** is quite a simple salad with only a few basic ingredients. Salads can be much more interesting. Take a look at the salads in photo **B** and see what has been included in them.

A   Is this what you think of as a salad?

Think about it!

1   **ABC** **TS** Look at the three ready-prepared salads in **B**.

   a) List the ingredients you can identify in each salad and then find out what the others are.

   b) Explain where the ingredients come from and why they have been used (colour, texture, flavour).

   c) Decide what type of person you think each salad is aimed at.

   d) Decide whether each salad includes a dressing. If so, what is it made from?

2   **TS** Which salad do you think is the most colourful? List the ingredients which make it colourful.

3   Which salad do you think would be the most crunchy? Explain why.

4   Which salad would you most like to eat? Explain your reasons.

5   If you have the opportunity to taste any ready-prepared salads, you could record your findings in a sensory analysis worksheet.

6   Can you add other, different salad ingredients to table **C**?

7   Imagine and then describe what would happen to your salad if you added cubes of cooked beetroot.

Ingredients in a salad can be classified according to their colour.

Red	tomatoes, red pepper
Yellow	sweetcorn, yellow pepper
Purple	radishes, beetroot, red onion, peppercorns
Brown	mushrooms
Green	lettuce, cucumber, green peppers, cress

C *Colours of salad ingredients*

(FPT) Mixing, cutting and heating

Experiment by mixing, cutting and heating ingredients and comparing colour and ratios. Look at preparing vegetables in different ways and how adding different amounts of ingredients makes a difference to salad.

Factfile

- Carrots are a colourful vegetable and a different colour from most salad ingredients.
- Colour is important when we choose ingredients for dishes.
- 'We eat with our eyes first'. What do you think this means?

Salad dressings

Some of the salads in **B** may have a dressing, that you cannot see in the picture. People use dressings to add flavour and texture to a salad. Often dressings are made of oil and other ingredients including herbs, vinegar, lemon juice, garlic and yoghurt. These ingredients make the dressing rich and flavoured.

D *Dressings are used to add flavour and texture to a salad*

Here is a typical vinaigrette dressing you may like to try on your salad.

Creamy coriander vinaigrette

Ingredients

4 tablespoons olive oil

4 tablespoons crème fraîche

4 teaspoons Dijon mustard

3 handfuls of chopped coriander

3–4 tablespoons lemon juice

Method

Put all the ingredients in a jam jar, screw on the lid firmly and shake well.

Factfile

- Salad dressings made of oil and water separate if left to stand. They must be shaken before use.
- Salad dressings such as mayonnaise that include egg yolk do not separate. The yolk helps the oil and water stick together. This is called **emulsification.**

(DMA) Design a new salad

D Design and make a new salad that looks good and will appeal to different people. The salad and its ingredients should follow the guidelines for healthy eating and could be sold in food stores.

Plenary

All this information and the experimental work you have carried out should make it easier to decide what types of ingredients or components should be in a salad.

Hygiene

Objectives

In this lesson you will learn more about hygiene and safety when handling food.

Key words

bacteria	micro-organisms, some of which may be harmful and contaminate foods (pathogenic bacteria), and some of which are useful, such as those in yoghurts
pathogenic	harmful
sterilised	heat-treated to remove all micro-organisms

Personal hygiene

The greatest enemies of the food room in school, your kitchen at home and a food factory are food poisoning **bacteria** (often called germs). Meet the 'bacteria team' in **A**.

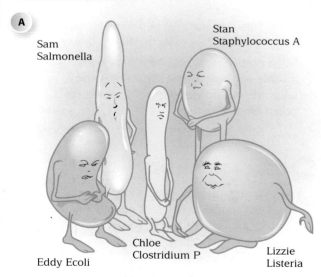

A

Sam
Salmonella

Stan
Staphylococcus A

Eddy Ecoli

Chloe
Clostridium P

Lizzie
Listeria

They want to give you food poisoning by growing on the food you eat. They are everywhere – in the air, on food, on you and on everything you touch.

But remember you can't see them. Even 400 million of these bacteria together are only the size of a sugar crystal. The good thing is that it is easy to stop them!

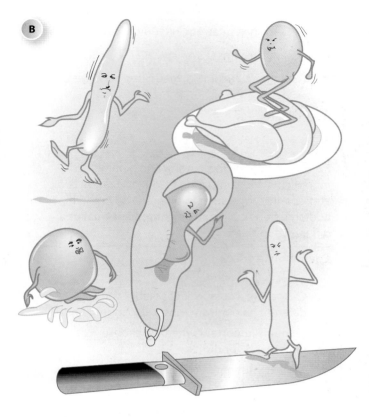

B

Looking after food

These bacteria need four things to grow and cause food poisoning.

- Moisture: bacteria particularly like moist food such as yoghurt and fish.

- Food: bacteria like lots of food but they are especially fond of meat, cream, cheese and so on. These are protein foods and are 'high risk' foods.

- Time: bacteria are like you, they need time to grow as well as food. They double in number every twenty minutes.

- Warmth: bacteria do not like cold temperatures such as the fridge (below 5°C) or freezer (below –18°C). They do not like very hot temperatures either. They like room temperature and body temperature.

We can stop these bacteria getting on food and then stop them growing if we follow some simple hygiene rules.

Factfile

Personal hygiene

- Wash your hands before and after handling food
- Wear an apron
- Don't cough or sneeze over food
- Cover cuts with a blue plaster
- Don't lick food, fingers or spoons during cooking

Looking after food

- Store moist foods in a fridge
- Cover all food
- Cook food until piping hot
- Cool hot food before you put it in the fridge
- Keep raw food away from cooked food

Equipment and environment

- Clean work surfaces
- Wash up all equipment in hot soapy water
- Use clean teatowels and dishcloths
- Keep the room clean, especially door handles and floors
- Be clean. Stop the bacteria team!

c *Workers in a food factory must wear protective clothing*

More about bacteria

- There are bacteria everywhere. Our skin is covered with them and our gut (intestines) are lined with them, as well as those that are in the air and on every surface. But not all bacteria are harmful. Some bacteria are useful to us. Lactobacillus bacteria are used to make yoghurt and cheese. Bifidobacteria are the bacteria in our gut that help keep us healthy. It is only the **pathogenic** bacteria that are harmful and bad for us.

Food factories

- Workers have to wear lots of protective clothing and are taught how to wash their hand properly.
- All equipment is **sterilised** everyday.
- Refrigerated lorries are used to transport 'high risk' foods from the factory to shops so the food is always cool.

Follow these rules to stop the bacteria team growing.

Think about it!

1. Where are bacteria found?
2. List some 'high risk' foods.
3. **TS** Explain why you think cross contamination is an easy way to cause food poisoning.
4. Find out more about Eddy (E coli), Lizzie (Listeria), Stan (Staphylococcus A), Chloe (Clostridium P), and Sam (Salmonella) by using the Internet or books.
5. **ICT** Design a poster illustrating one hygiene rule. You could use ICT. The poster should be colourful and easy to read from a distance,.
6. There are some 'good' bacteria in foods. Can you list some foods that have good bacteria in them?

Plenary

You should now know how important hygiene is when working with food. You know the hygiene rules to follow in a food room.

Looking at snacks

Objectives

- In this lesson you will:
- find out what a designer needs to think about when designing new products
- think about people's needs when designing.

Key words

snack	a food product which consists of a casing (outside) and filling (inside)
component parts	what a product is made from
consumers	people who buy and use food products
designers	people in the food industry who develop new food products
analyse	look carefully at and find a way to solve a problem

A

B

Look at the photos in **A**. Who do you think these **snacks** are for? Are they for any particular person or just people in general? Look closely at the products and see if you can identify the **component parts** (outer casing, inner filling mix). You could record your findings on a table similar to the one in **B**.

What do you think the **designers** were thinking about when they designed these products? Do you think that they thought about any of the criteria shown in **C**?

Lifestyle- working and busy, low income, enjoys cooking

Diet- vegetarian, healthy, allergies, gluten free, 'standard'

Other- tradition, culture, fashion, travel

NEEDS

Snack requirments- main meal, party, quick snack, lunchtime

Age/sex- female, male, adult, older person, small child

C *Finding out about consumer demand*

Think about it!

1. Look at diagram **C**. Think carefully and then add some more suggestion to this diagram.
2. For each of the snacks you have considered in table **B**, decide who they are for and which criteria have been used. Write down the decisions you have reached.
3. Write a design specification for each of the products listing the criteria you that you think the product had to meet. Look back at Unit 2 for help with design specification.

	Product name	Size	Type of pastry	Filling includes
A				
B				
C				

The products in **D** were designed to respond to the needs and demands of consumers.

The person in **E** needs to think carefully before acting on her idea. What do you think that she needs to do?

- Talk to children of the right age to find out what they like.
- Investigate the kinds of foods in their lunchboxes already.

I've got a great idea for packed lunches

- Measure their hands – small hands, small snack, easier to eat.
- Measure their lunch boxes to see what size foods will fit.

If you had to find out about **consumers'** needs, what would you do? How would you start? Asking questions is one way to start. You could compile a simple questionnaire to find information out about the likes and dislikes of the appropriate age group. Think about the kinds of questions you could ask. Closed questions give a range of answers to choose from, such as 'Which casing do you like best: shortcrust pastry, puff pastry or filo pastry?' Open questions don't suggest answers – the person makes up their own answer.

It is easier to use closed questions as you do not get such a wide variety of answers to your questions. When you have asked the questions, the most important part is to **analyse** the responses. This means to look at all the replies, count them up and decide which were the most popular answers. In this way you can be surer that your new product meets a consumer need.

Think about it!

1 **ICT** After carrying out a shop survey (try on-line shopping or 'New Foods' CD-ROM) make a list of sweet and savoury snacks that are available.

2 Look at the photograph in **D**.

   a) Explain what you think the needs were.

   b) This product has been successful. Explain why you think it meets the needs of consumers.

   c) What do you think caused the demand for this product?

   D d) Suggest some new products that consumers may want to buy. Explain why you think they will want to buy these products.

Plenary

It is important to understand that food products are designed to make a profit for the manufacturer. They are not just manufactured in the hope that they will sell.

Use the information on consumer demand to help remind you about what you need to think about when designing new products for different groups of consumers.

Learning about casings and fillings

Objectives

In this lesson you will:

● identify ingredients in different food products

● try out a range of practical skills.

Key words

bind make a mixture stick together using another ingredient

Every food product that has been designed has a set of ingredients. If these ingredients are identified it will help you to make or design a similar product.

The snacks we are considering have their own list of ingredients, which are used for particular reasons.

● The casing is used to keep the filling together so that the snack can be held by hand. An example of a casing is pastry.

● The filling usually has a cheaper ingredient to 'bulk it up', for example potato. It has something to stick or **bind** or thicken the filling such as sauce. It may also contain a protein food such as cheese, meat or pulses.

There are also other things to consider which we looked at under the criteria for the snack requirement. Go back and have a look at these (page 20–1).

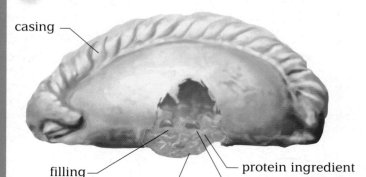

A

casing

filling

sauce

protein ingredient

bulking ingredient

Product analysis

Let us look at a similar snack product and see how it can be evaluated.

B

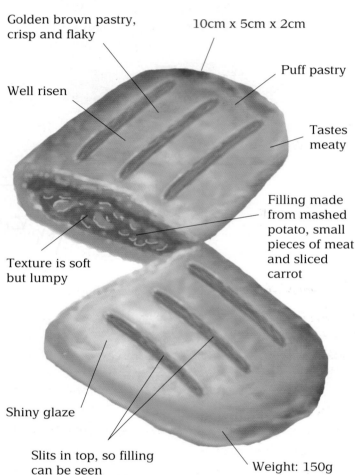

Golden brown pastry, crisp and flaky

10cm x 5cm x 2cm

Well risen

Puff pastry

Tastes meaty

Texture is soft but lumpy

Filling made from mashed potato, small pieces of meat and sliced carrot

Shiny glaze

Slits in top, so filling can be seen

Weight: 150g

Making a snack

D To make a snack like the one in **B** you could use a ready-made pastry and filling to learn more about casings and fillings. You could make a different shape and size and give it a different glaze.

Looking at snacks

There are many food products that could be categorized as snacks. Study table **C**, which gives information about different types of snack products.

Type of snack	Casing		Possible fillings	Method of cooking
Samosa	Filo pastry		Potato, peas, prawns, meat, spices	Deep-fat fry, bake
Spring roll	Filo pastry		Bean sprouts, peppers, meat, prawns, seasoning	Deep-fat fry
Dim sum	Filo pastry		Fish, meat	Steam
Calzone	Bread dough		Cheese, tomato, vegetables, meat, prawns, herbs	Bake
Cornish pasty	Shortcrust pastry		Potato, carrot, meat	Bake
Sausage roll	Puff pastry		Sausage meat	Bake

c *Types of snacks*

You can see there are many sorts of casing that could be used:

- filo pastry – originally from the east Mediterranean – thin layers of pastry, low fat, crispy when baked or fried, soft when steamed
- bread dough – bread mixture
- shortcrust pastry – thin, short pastry, baked, fat content quite high
- puff pastry – thin layers of pastry, high fat, baked.

Many times the method of cooking determines the outcome. For example when filo pastry is baked or fried the outcome is light, golden brown and crispy, but when steamed the pastry is white in colour and moist.

Methods of cooking are classified according to how the heat is applied. The outcomes can be very different! Consider the difference between pastry cooked using moist (with liquid) methods such as steaming or boiling compared with dry cooking methods such as baking and frying.

Think about it!

1 **TS** What were the essential criteria for your snack product? What did you want your snack to be like?

2 **PA** Evaluate your snack in the same way as in **B**. Your criteria will help you with this evaluation. Was it successful? How could you improve it?

3 Complete a star profile of your product using these descriptors: crisp, golden brown, shiny, well-shaped.

4 Use a recipe book to carry out research into pastry products. From your findings list six different pastry products and say how they are cooked.

5 **CT** Find out what safety precautions you should follow when frying foods.

Plenary

You should have found out a lot of information about the casings and fillings for snacks by product analysis and focused practical tasks.

Modelling

The fillings for snacks are as limitless as your imagination! Look at the example of a savoury filling in **A**.

A modelling exercise

There are so many different foods that could be used for fillings and so many different ways of combining them that it could take forever to find the best combination if you made just one idea each practical session. The best way to try out the most ideas is to use **prototypes** by modelling small quantities of fillings at the same time.

Here is an example of some Year 7 students who have been modelling. Martin and Anna have decided on four different ideas for their pasties. Their teacher has told them to use not more than eight different ingredients because they must think about the cost of all the ingredients and they must also be able to carry them to school! The teacher will provide some spices and herbs for flavouring, and will also provide potato flakes that can be used to bind the ingredients together (**B**).

Martin and Anna both prepare their ingredients by slicing, chopping, grating and mixing. Each bowl has a different combination of ingredients. Martin's first bowl has onion, sweetcorn, chicken, Cajun spices, salt and pepper and potato flakes. Anna's bowl has an interesting combination of tomato, onion, carrot, peas and cheese with potato flakes and salt and pepper.

Martin and Anna both use ready-rolled puff pastry circles. They use special pasty makers to seal the pasty. Anna uses some extra pastry to make letters to identify which pasty is which, while Martin uses shapes (**C**).

The pasties are baked in the oven and frozen until the next lesson. The whole class then carries out tasting tests on all the pasties. They save half of each pasty to take home. Martin's favourite pasty is the one with a filling of ham, peas, onion, curry powder and potato flakes (**D**).

Martin and Anna learned a lot from this practical exercise and were quickly able to decide on their best filling.

A

Think about it!

1   **ABC** Look at **A**. List the food or ingredients used in the filling and describe how it is prepared for use.

2   **ABC** Explain why each ingredient is used in the filling.

3   Here are examples of foods which could be used for filling snacks. One example of a new idea is baked beans, ham and mashed potato. What combination of fillings can you suggest?

You could add some extra filling suggestions of you own but don't use more than three different types and remember the component parts that should be included. (Look back at **A** on page 22.)

boiled potatoes	peas	bean sprouts	parsnip
sausages	baked beans	mashed potato	sprouts
tuna	cheese	onion	bacon
chicken	apple	Quorn™	prawns
steak	swede	ham	pickles
carrots	mushrooms	peppers	salmon
sweet potatoes	apple	pasta	leeks

4   **D** **ABC** Sketch and annotate three examples of new fillings that you could make yourself. For each one suggest a name for the snack, the type of casing you could use around the outside and how the filling might be cooked.

5   **TS** What changes could be made to the preparation of the ingredients to change their appearance?

6   Martin and Anna modelled fillings. What other modelling practical tasks could you carry out to help you design a pasty?

Plenary

Now you have seen how you could model different prototypes you can plan and carry out your own modelling exercise. Modelling ideas can be done practically, as annotated drawings or as written descriptions. They are quick and easy ways to find out what ideas are successful.

How do manufacturers make pastry products?

Objectives

In this lesson you will learn how pastry products are made in industry.

Key words

one-off production	one product is made at a time
mass production	the same product is produced in large quantities
production line	a moving conveyor belt often used to assemble products
batch production	a specific quantity of one product is produced in a single production run

You have modelled prototypes to find the best idea for a new filling for a pasty. This kind of experimental work happens in industry too. Most food factories have a test kitchen where new ideas are tried out and tested. A product development manager usually runs the kitchen and plans all the work. Any work carried out is carefully recorded so that the products can be made again to exactly the same size, shape, weight and flavour. All the cooking temperatures and times are noted for the same reasons

A great deal of work will go into producing a new food product: experimenting with different ingredients, testing to see how long the product will keep and working out its nutritional content. Only about one out of every fifty prototypes is developed into a product for the supermarket or shop shelves.

A test kitchen is like a Food Technology room or your kitchen at home. There is ordinary food preparation equipment and perhaps some food processors to save time. The oven is family sized. Only a small quantity of the food product is made. Some smaller companies or bakeries may use this test kitchen to produce individual products as well, for example a special birthday cake or wedding cake. This is called **one-off production** because there is

A   *This cake is an example of one-off production*

only one product at the end. This type of production is skilled and the product can be expensive especially if a skilled worker, like a chef, is making the product.

Mass production

Once a new product has been developed it will be mass produced. **Mass production** is when a lot of the same product is made in one factory all at the same time. Specialist machinery is used and few people take part in the process. The product is made on a **production line**, which is usually controlled by

B   *A production line of sausage rolls*

computers. **B, C , D, E** and **F** show examples of a production line.

1 Flour, water and oil are piped into a large mixer (the amount is weighed and controlled by computer) and mixed to a dough.

2 The pastry is rolled onto the line by machine.

3 Sausage meat has been put into a depositor.

4 The depositor pipes out a continuous line of sausage meat onto the pastry below.

5 The pastry is cut and folded over the sausage meat.

6 The rolls are cut into 10cm lengths.

7 Egg glaze is put onto the rolls.

8 The sausage rolls are baked in a tunnel oven (temperature controlled by computer).

9 The sausage rolls are cooled before they are packed.

10 The sausage rolls are packaged, labelled, date stamped and delivered to a shop or supermarket.

C *Preparing sausage meat*

D *Meat being piped into pastry*

E *Sausage rolls cooling*

Batch production

Not all food products that you buy in the shops are mass produced. Some foods are **batch produced**. This is when a single food product is made at one time, but not in massive quantities. Another batch of a different product can then be made using the same machinery. A good example is a small bakery that makes a batch of pastry products each morning. For example, they make 40 sausage rolls, 20 beef pies, 40 Cornish pasties and 20 cheese and onion pies. Less room is needed for this type of production and the equipment is less expensive.

F

Whether mass production or batch production is used by a manufacturer depends upon the quantity that is needed.

Think about it!

1 (TS) Plan out the batch production or mass production of your snack product. Describe how you will make sure you ensure the right quality each time.

2 Sketch the equipment you would use to mass produce your snack product.

Plenary

You have learned how food products are made in quantity.

Desserts

Objectives

In this lesson you will:

- find out about the functions of different ingredients in a dessert
- learn how ingredients thicken and set.

Key words

coagulation	the process by which a liquid turns to a solid as the protein sets
gelatinisation	thickening process caused by heating a liquid and a starch

Is **A** your ideal dessert? How would you decide on:

- the layers for a chilled dessert
- the appearance and texture of the layers
- the nutrients in the layers
- how the layers are made and the function of their ingredients
- the design criteria are you could follow?

You could make a better choice of layers if you had more information!

A

Name of ingredient	Set or thickened by
Cream	Thickened by adding air
Fresh sliced fruit	
Custard	Starch and/or eggs used to thicken
Meringue	Egg white is thickened by adding air and then set by cooking (heating)
Fruit puree	Fruit mashed to thicken
Biscuit 'base' mixture	Fat (butter or margarine) set by solidifying
Flavoured jelly	Gelatine sets the liquid
Whisked sponge	The mixture is thickened by adding air and then set by cooking
Instant dessert	Instantly set by modified starch
Yoghurt	Milk is thickened by 'good' bacteria

Making the different layers

Thickening

- Cream becomes thick foam when it is whipped. Air beaten into the cream makes bubbles. The protein in the cream changes its shape and surrounds the air bubbles. This protects the air bubbles so that they do not burst. The fat in the cream sticks to the protected bubbles and keeps the structure.

- Yoghurt is fermented milk thickened by the **coagulation** of protein in the milk. A culture made of two good bacteria (*lactobacillus bulgaricus* and *streptococcus thermophilis*) breaks down the protein in milk so it coagulates. These bacteria also produce acid and carbon dioxide in the milk.

- Fruit puree is made when fruit is chopped and mashed to form a thick sauce. The cell walls of the fruit break down or dissolve and the structure

B   *Thickening cream by whipping*

Cream

Cream being whisked

air bubbles

Fully whisked

protein in cream

air bubbles

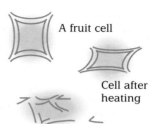
A fruit cell

Cell after heating

Cell after mechanical action

C   *Thickening fruit by mashing*

of the fruit changes. This can be done by heating, by mechanical action or by both processes.

- Some sauces, such as custard, are thickened by starch (in flour and cornflour). When starch is heated in liquid the liquid begins to pass through the walls of the starch granules, which slowly become swollen and burst. The starch absorbs the liquid and thickens. This thickening process is known as **gelatinisation**.

- Some starches are modified (changed in some way) so that they thicken without heating. They can instantly thicken. Instant desserts, such as Angel Delight and Instant Whip, use these modified starches. This kind of modified starch is called instant or pregelatinised starch because it has already been thickened in water by heating and dried into tiny granules.

Setting

An easy way to set some mixtures is to use a solid fat like margarine or butter. A biscuit layer is made in this way. It is a very hard layer but makes a good contrast in texture to other layers. The fat is heated until it becomes a liquid, added to biscuits crumbs and allowed to solidify. Melted chocolate would have the same effect when mixed with biscuit crumbs. Why do you think this is so?

The main method of setting components is to use protein and its coagulating (gelation) properties. Two types of protein can be used: gelatine and egg protein.

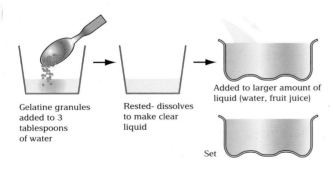

Gelatine granules added to 3 tablespoons of water

Rested- dissolves to make clear liquid

Added to larger amount of liquid (water, fruit juice)

Set

D *Gelatine can be used to set a liquid*

Gelatine is a protein extracted from animals (there is a vegetarian alternative made from seaweed). When it is added to water and heated it swells up and dissolves to make a clear liquid. When cooled it becomes a solid gel. This is called gelation. You can buy a packet of ready flavoured jelly that has gelatine in it or you can use powdered or leaf gelatine and

add your own flavouring by using a fruit juice or fruit puree as the liquid. You could also add extras to your jelly such as fruit or substitute milk or cream for the liquid (**D**).

Eggs (protein) set mixtures by coagulating during cooking, for example, meringues or sponge cakes. Above 63°C they go hard. In both these cases the eggs are thickened using air by whisking. Egg white can hold up to seven times its own volume of air. This is because the protein can stretch to trap lots of air bubbles. Meringues are made in this way. Even whole eggs can hold a lot of air. Whole eggs are whisked to trap air and are the main raising agent for whisked (fat-less) sponges such as swiss rolls. Once both mixtures are thickened, they are cooked so that the stretched protein sets into a solid structure. It coagulates.

You will have a better understanding of the function of these ingredients if you carry out a focused practical task. You could make swiss roll, lemon meringue pie, jellies, custards and instant desserts. Record the recipe and method of any product you make and the function of each ingredient.

Think about it!

1 List other desserts that use eggs to make them set.

2 Can you include a savoury dish that is set in the same way?

3 **ABC** List some savoury food products you can buy which instantly thicken with hot or cold water.

4 Can you think of a non-food product that uses instant starch?

Plenary

It is important to understand setting and thickening. You should know how to use different ingredients to set and thicken the different layers.

Exploring materials

Objectives

In this lesson you will:

- understand the functions of nutrients
- increase your awareness of the origins of different foods and ingredients
- use a nutritional analysis program
- look at changing the nutritional profile of foods

Key words

nutrients	components of food that do particular jobs in the body. The main nutrients are carbohydrates, fats, proteins, vitamins and minerals
nutritional profile/ analysis	using a computer program to find the nutritional value of food products

A

Have you thought about how healthy the dessert in **A** might be?

B

Name of ingredient	Origin or made from	Includes nutrients
Cream	Fresh milk	Fat
Fresh sliced fruit	Fresh whole fruit	Vitamin C, NSP, sugar
Custard	Milk, sugar, custard powder (thickener and flavour)	Calcium, protein, sugar, starch
Meringue	Egg white, sugar	Sugar, little protein
Fruit puree	Fresh or canned fruit, sugar	Vitamin C, NSP, sugar
Biscuit 'base' mixture	Crushed sweet biscuits, margarine/butter, sugar	Sugar, fat, starch
Flavoured jelly	Gelatine (setting), water, flavour, sugar	Sugar,
Whisked sponge	Margarine, sugar, eggs	Fat, sugar, protein
Instant dessert	Modified/pregelatinised starch	
Yoghurt	Milk, 'good' bacteria, sugar, flavour, (fresh fruit?)	Sugar, calcium

Foods and food products contain different and differing amounts of **nutrients** as you can see from table **B**. Nutrients can be divided into five main groups depending on their function in the body.

- Protein builds new cells and new tissues. It is found mainly in meat, cheese, eggs, milk, fish, and pulses (beans, nuts and lentils).
- Carbohydrates such as starch, NSP (non-starch polysaccharide or dietary fibre) and sugar provide us with energy. These are found in sugary foods, bread, potatoes, pasta, rice and cereals.
- Fat is needed to give us energy and is found in oils, cooking fats, dairy products and fatty foods.
- Vitamins are identified by letters – A, B, C, D, E, K. We need each of them and each one has a different function.
- Minerals such as calcium, iron, phosphorous, sodium, zinc have a different jobs in keeping the body healthy.

Remember the recommendations suggested by the balanced plate? Which nutrients do you think that it is better to eat in moderation? It's not as easy as you think to eat healthily because most foods contain many nutrients not just one. Also different people need different amounts of nutrients depending on their age, sex and lifestyle.

Nutritional profiles

Listing ingredients and their nutrients is one way of identifying the nutrients in foods and food products (**B**). Another way is to use a nutritional analysis software program to produce a **nutritional profile/analysis**. **C** gives an example of the nutritional analysis of an apple pie.

Ingredients for apple pie

Pastry

200g plain flour

100g block margarine

Filling

600g stewed apples

50g white sugar

Nutrition Information - Apple pie		
	Typical values	
	per 100 g	per serving 158 g
Energy	800 Kj 191 Kcal	1264 Kj 302 Kcal
Protein	2.19 g	3.46 g
Carbohydrate	27.1 g	42.8 g
of which sugar	11.1 g	17.5 g
Fat	8.93 g	14.1 g
of which saturates	3.24 g	5.12 g
Fibre (NSP)	1.6 g	2.53 g
Sodium	0.09 g	0.14 g
Iron	0.52 mg	0.81 mg
Calcium	32.5 mg	51.4 mg
Vitamin A	84.7 ug	134 ug
Thiamine (B1)	0.07 mg	0.11 mg
Riboflavin (B2)	0.01 mg	0.02 mg
Niacin	0.42 mg	0.67 mg
Vitamin C	6.95 mg	11 mg
Vitamin D	0.84 ug	1.32 ug

C The nutritional analysis of the apple pie

As the ingredients in a product are changed so the nutritional profile changes as well. However you can't just change the ingredients for something else you fancy putting in. You have to use ingredients that have the same functional property. You can't change Edam cheese for apples, or margarine for plain flour but you could change the Edam cheese for Cheddar cheese or the margarine for butter. Remember that changing ingredients may change the flavour, texture and colour of the product.

FPT Experimenting with ingredients

You may have the opportunity to experiment with the nutritional value and function of one of the dessert layers, for example, flavoured jelly.

Think about it!

1 **ABC** Discuss with a partner whether you think that the designers of desserts take into consideration the nutritional value of the product. List the points you come up with.

2 **TS** How well does the dessert in **A** fit into the suggestions made by the balanced plate? What could you do to make the dessert healthier?

3 **TS** Can you explain why the bacteria in the yoghurt have been called 'good'?

4 **TS** Consider a trifle and a cheesecake. Identify the nutrients which each contains. You may need to use a reference book or information provided by your teacher. Use a table like the one in **B** to record your findings.

5 **ICT** Use a nutritional analysis program to analyse other desserts your teacher suggests. Firstly you will need to find recipes for similar desserts from a recipe book. Find out which nutrients are contained in each dessert. Select the following information and record it: which dessert has the most fat, which has the most sugar, which the most Vitamin C.

6 **ABC** From the information you have gathered, which dessert do you think is the most healthy? Give reasons for your answer.

7 **D** Choose one of the other components from the dessert and see if you can suggest changes and alternatives which could be tried. Make sure you record your work.

Plenary

On these pages you should have learned about the five main groups of nutrients and their functions, you should also be able to use a nutritional analysis program to model ideas.

Tasting and testing desserts

Objectives

In this lesson you will:

- use sensory descriptors
- use sensory analysis and preference tests to help make decisions
- finish and decorate a dessert.

Key words

taste panel	a group of people who taste food and drink and give views on characteristics, for example, taste and texture
ranking test	placing samples of food or drink in order of preference
rating test	giving products a score on a scale of 1 to 5

A

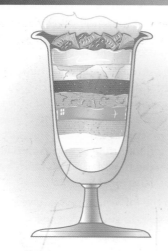

Have you thought about tasting and testing desserts? This might be the best part!

Before making your own dessert, it is a good idea to look at the different components in detail. This will help you make up your mind about which layers to include and the best way to make them. Looking in shops and at recipe books you'll see that custard can be made in a number of ways: 'original' custard made from eggs, milk and sugar; a packet mix; tinned or ready-made fresh custard. How do you know which is best or which one you like? Here are some ways of making decisions about which either you or a number of people prefer.

Name of ingredient	Sensory descriptors
Cream	White, creamy, smooth, sweet
Fresh sliced fruit	Crunchy, fresh, colourful, juicy, crisp, sweet, sharp
Custard	Smooth, yellow, set, wobbly, thick, creamy
Meringue	Sweet, crispy, brittle, crunchy, bitty
Fruit puree	Smooth, bitty, sweet, colourful, sloppy, runny, fruity
Biscuit 'base' mixture	Hard, crunchy, sweet, gritty
Flavoured jelly	Sweet, fruity, wobbly, see through, set
Whisked sponge	Soft, spongy, sweet, crispy, golden brown
Instant dessert	Colourful, sweet, soft, bubbly,
Yoghurt	Sweet, sour, smooth, lumpy, thin, creamy, runny

B   *Sensory description*

Working with food always involves looking at it and tasting it to make sure it is what consumers want and like! Table **B** shows sensory descriptors describing the different layers in the dessert. All the senses are used when tasting and testing food. We can group the words like this:

- looks/appearance
- taste/flavour
- aroma/smell
- texture/mouth feel
- touch/feel.

Think about it!

ABC Imagine your favourite food. Write down a list of sensory words that you could use to describe it. Think about the shape, colour and size before you start on the smell, flavour and texture. Share your description with someone else and see if they can guess what the food is without you telling them beforehand.

Tasting

Set up a **taste panel** in order to conduct a **sensory analysis** of the product. Remember the following rules:

- set up a quiet area where you (or other tasters) will not be disturbed
- have a glass of water to sip between samples
- use small quantities of food with clean utensils each time
- do not influence tasters by naming the product, use a code or symbol instead
- do not put dirty spoons into the samples
- make sure you have a way of recording what you and other tasters think of the product.

Testing

You may also want to try a **ranking** or **rating** test to find out what type of custard people like best. Ranking tests ask tasters to put food in order of preference, starting with the one they like best. You can use a table like C.

Taste the samples and put them into the order you like best		
Sample code	Order	Comment
Sample ☐		
Sample ○		
Sample △		

C   Ranking test table for different types of custard

Rating tests are used to show how much a product is liked or disliked. You can use a table like **D**.

Taste the samples and tick the appropriate box					
Sample code	1	2	3	4	5
Sample ☐					
Sample ○					
Sample △					

1 = dislike a lot   4 = like a little
2 = dislike a little   5 = like a lot.
3 = neither like nor dislike

D   Rating test table for different types of custard

Record all your results so you can make an informed decision about the type of custard you could use in a dessert which you may design and make. You may want to do this kind of analysis with a number of the different layers – base, fruit puree or instant dessert.

Decorating and finishing the dessert

Look around at all the fabulous desserts you can buy in shops and supermarkets. The decoration used makes them attractive to different people. A plain, sophisticated finish may be for an adult market while a dessert piled with piped cream and sprinkled with hundreds and thousands could be designed for a younger person.

Cream makes good decoration, but there are several types of cream to choose from which have different purposes. If your choice included single cream, double cream or whipping cream which one would you choose for the top of your dessert?

FPT Decorating a dessert

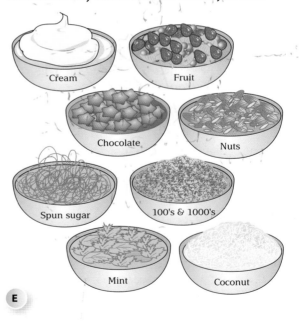

E shows a variety of toppings which could be used to finish off any dessert. Which would you use?

Cream · Fruit · Chocolate · Nuts · Spun sugar · 100's & 1000's · Mint · Coconut

E

Plenary

You should now know much more about sensory analysis and alternative ways of decorating a dessert.

Chilling and freezing

Food preservation

Many desserts are chilled. Chilling helps to keep the structure of your dessert but it also helps preserve it. Preservation makes food last longer. It has a longer **shelf-life**. Desserts can be chilled or frozen which are both important ways of preserving food.

Chilling

Chilling extends the shelf-life of food for a short period of time. Chilling:

- has become very popular over the last fifteen years
- slows bacterial growth
- does not change the flavour, colour, texture, shape or nutrition of food.

Chilled foods:

- last up to five days after being made
- must be stored between 0°C and 3°C
- are always sold from chilled cabinets and must be kept in a fridge at home

A *There is a wide range of chilled desserts available*

- are often thought to be better quality than frozen foods
- do not need to be defrosted before eating.

Freezing

Freezing preserves food for a period of time between one week and one year. It extends the shelf-life of food for a long time. Freezing:

- has become the most popular domestic method of food preservation
- stops bacterial growth
- means the water in the food changes to ice crystals.

Frozen foods:

- must be stored between –18°C and –29°C
- often needs defrosting before eating (not ice cream!)
- are sometimes not as good quality as chilled foods because cell damage can occur in soft fruit, and sauces collapse or leak water.

B

Look at the strawberries in **B**. If you have tasted them, or have the opportunity in class to taste them, describe their different textures and explain what you think has happened to the strawberries and why.

Choosing equipment

What equipment will you use to produce a dessert?
You might not have a choice but the equipment you
could use is shown in table **C**.

Process	Equipment	
Whisk	Fork, balloon whisk, rotary whisk, electric hand whisk	
Reduce biscuits to crumbs	Rolling pin and plastic bag, food processor	
Puree fruit	Sieve, blender/food processor	
Separate eggs	Shell, hand, separator	
Melt gelatine or chocolate	Pan over boiling water or microwave	
Decorate with cream	Spoon or piping bag	

C

Think about it!

1 Visit a supermarket and look at deserts in the chiller cabinet and in the freezer cabinet. Compare the variety of frozen desserts available to the variety of chilled desserts. Record your findings as a chart. You might want to construct a database.

2 **ABC** Choose one of the FPTs you have completed and write down the equipment you used. Explain if your choice of equipment was correct or would you use a different piece of equipment next time?

3 Choose two other processes and evaluate the equipment in table **C** for those processes. Think about the cost, storage, safety, time involved and skills needed. You can evaluate this equipment practically to see if your choice of equipment is most effective or efficient.

4 **FPT** Working in groups, investigate different methods of whisking egg whites. Use the four pieces of equipment listed in table **C** to whisk one egg white. Time how long this takes and record the results.

    a) Which is the quickest method of whisking egg whites?

    b) Which is the most labour-saving method of whisking egg whites?

    c) Does the size of the mixing bowl used make any difference to the time taken to whisk?

    d) Which is the most expensive piece of equipment used to whisk the egg white?

    e) If you broke the yolk when separating an egg, with some of the yolk getting into the white, did the yolk affect the way the white behaved when it was whisked ? Do you know why?

5 **TS** Decide which is the easiest, safest and quickest way of separating eggs.

DMA Design a dessert

D Design a layered chilled dessert containing fruit for one person. Consider presenting it in a transparent container to show off the layered effect.

Plenary

You should understand about chilling and freezing and how to choose equipment.

Lifecycles

The **lifecycle** of a product is the time from when it was invented and made to the time it is no longer made. For example a product may be withdrawn from production (stop being made) because sales have dropped and the company that made it is no longer making a profit.

A   KitKat's now come in a variety of shapes and sizes

The lifecycle of a favourite chocolate bar

KitKats have been sold since 1935 and were one of the first chocolate bars to be made. They were originally called Chocolate Crisp. Today there is a wide range of biscuit bars available. This means that there is competition between manufacturers. Nestlé, who manufacture KitKats, have had to think of different ways to encourage people to buy them. They have redesigned and updated their KitKat brand to include different varieties with the same brand name and a similar theme. For example, you can now buy:

- chunky KitKats
- four-finger KitKats
- two-fingers KitKats
- limited edition and flavoured KitKats
- KitKat ice cream bars.

What other varieties of KitKat might Nestlé bring out in the future to persuade consumers to buy the brand – KitKat drinks, cakes or desserts?

Pasta

There are many other products that have been changed or redesigned to increase their life. Pasta is one example. It was cooked, mixed with a tomato sauce and tinned to make it into a convenience food so more people would buy it.

B   *Food manufacturers use the latest children's television shows or films to increase the sales of these products.*

Yorkshire puddings

Traditional Yorkshire puddings are not eaten as much as in the past as fewer families now sit down to a traditional Sunday roast. Someone thought of an excellent idea to extend the lifecycle of this tasty food by making the product bigger and serving it with a variety of fillings in the middle.

C   *These 'filled' Yorkshire puddings have become very popular for pub lunches and as ready meals and have even been adapted as sophisticated starters.*

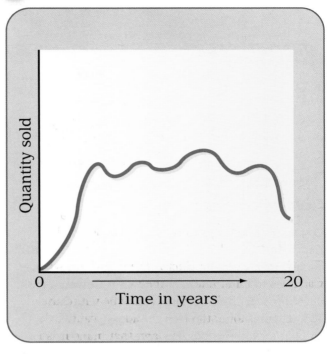

 D *Vol au vent cases, made from puff pastry, are available ready-made*

Puff pastry

Another example of how a product has been slightly changed to increase sales is puff pastry. It is quite difficult to roll out any pastry thinly and evenly so now puff pastry is available ready-rolled and cut out into shapes.

Product lifecycle curves

If a product is not developed in any way, its lifecycle will look like **E**. If a product is developed into different varieties or different sizes and shapes and packaged differently, its life cycle might look like **F**.

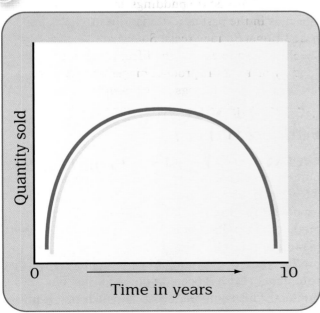

Food manufacturers find ways of tapping into people's different and changing lifestyles by looking at people profiles and then altering their food products. (This is explained on pages 38–9.)

Think about it!

1 **TS** Think about other brands that have been recently updated. Make a list of products and how they have been redesigned

2 **TS** Explain how pasta, Yorkshire pudding and puff pastry have been changed to prevent a drop in sales and extend their shelf life.

3 **TS** Think about the flapjack. Explain how it has been developed from a traditional cake baked in the home to how it is today. Think about packaging and extra ingredients that have been added.

4 **D** Identify a famous product and imagine you have been asked to develop a new version of it. Write down the key characteristics that you should keep in the new product and then write down some ideas for your new version.

Plenary

You can see that there are different ways that products are changed to help extend their lifecycle.

Batch production

Cowman's sausage shop

Cowman's famous sausage shop in Clitheroe, Lancashire makes 72 varieties of sausages. Cowman's is known all over the world and people travel long distances to buy these sausages. Cliff Cowman took the shop over from his father in 1984. His father, Ted, had started to develop the sausage side of his butcher's shop in 1986. He developed ten varieties. In the 18 years that Cliff has been running the shop, he has introduced 62 more varieties at an average of three or four a year. The most popular sausage is Cumberland. Other varieties include: pork, apple and mint; lamb and rosemary, egg and bacon and wild boar. 65 per cent of Cliff's business comes from sausage sales, so you can see how important it has been for Cliff's business to develop many different sausage varieties.

A *Cliff Cowman makes 72 varieties of sausages*

Farmhouse Biscuits

Farmhouse Biscuits originated in 1962 when farmers, Mr and Mrs McKiver, were suffering from a particularly bad winter. Livestock were freezing to death and the hens were not laying. As Mr McKiver didn't have a lot of produce to sell on his market stall, his wife baked some cakes and about ten varieties of biscuits using her mother's old recipes. The biscuits quickly became very popular so more were made each week. Soon the farm buildings were converted into a bakery to cope with the demand for these biscuits. In 1978 the business moved out of the farmhouse into a bigger factory. Today over 300 varieties of biscuits are made. Twenty per cent of sales are to overseas buyers and the biscuits are sold all over the UK.

B

Batch production

Cowman's and Farmhouse Biscuits can easily and quickly develop a new variety of their product. They can do this because they batch produce their products. You were introduced to the different methods of production in Unit 3 (pages 26–7). Food manufacturers who mass produce find it difficult to produce varieties because they use so much specialist equipment that has been designed for just one product. This equipment costs so much that it must be kept constantly in use to make a profit.

Batch production is a method of making a smaller quantity of identical products. Batch production is often carried out in small bakeries. In this situation the equipment can easily be used to make another small quantity of a variety of a product. Fewer machines and more people are used in batch production so batch production is more flexible.

C

Cliff uses a mixing machine for all his sausages. He fills the extruder by hand and once the mixture has been forced out into the skins, he 'links' the sausages together (see **C**).

Farmhouse Biscuits use computerised scales to accurately weigh out the ingredients for their biscuits. They use large industrial mixers shown in **D**, so that larger quantities than one person could mix can be made. Big shelf ovens are used that rotate the trays for even baking and the cooled biscuits are tipped onto a conveyor belt and packed by hand.

The equipment used in batch production is bigger than that used in your home or in the school food room but much smaller than the equipment used in mass production. It can be used in such a way as to enable variations to be produced with people helping this to happen. For example Cliff can either 'link' short chipolata sausages or long normal-sized sausages.

Think about it!

1   **ABC** Explain in your own words why food manufacturers who batch produce products can quickly make a new variety of a product.

2   **TS** Because more and more consumers buy their meat at supermarkets, many butchers have gone out of business. Explain why this has not happened with Cliff Cowman and his butcher's shop.

Plenary

You should understand that using batch production means manufacturers are flexible and can produce a variety of products.

D

Developing products

Objectives

In this lesson you will:

- learn about people profiles
- learn how people profiles can help food manufacturers to design variations of a product.

Key words

people profiles	information about target consumers
standard product	a product in everyday use
specification	exact details of what a product should be like

People profiles

Food manufacturers find ways of tapping into people's different and changing lifestyles. When they alter their food products or develop new ones, they use **people profiles** to help them with decisions. Supermarkets can already define the type of person you are and the type of foods you are likely to buy just by looking at the foods which you and your family buy each week. Loyalty cards allow larger supermarkets to collect data about shopping habits and changing tastes and needs. So is it easy to decide what a twenty-five-year-old single man or a family group of mother, father and three children (aged two, five and ten) will buy from a supermarket, or what influence a fourteen-year-old teenager will have on the family's weekly shopping. Try to describe the type of profile your family group has. Is it:

- busy, with little time to shop?
- shopping daily, weekly or monthly?
- buying individual desserts aimed at young children?
- wanting foods for packed lunches?
- buying fresh or tinned fruit or something else?

Remember all the products in a shop or supermarket are someone's favourites or aimed at a particular person or group of people. Look at the food products in **A**, **B**, **C** and **D** and decide who they may be aimed at. Write down your decisions giving reasons for them.

A

B

C

D

🟡 *Making biscuits*

Here is a basic biscuit recipe using the creaming method.

Use this as your standard product or find another basic biscuit recipe using the rubbed in or melting method. You could even make something else such as cakes, sausages or burgers.

The specification for the biscuits (what they should be like after they have been cooked) is:

- 🔵 golden-brown colour
- 🔵 crisp, crunchy texture
- 🔵 medium-sweet taste
- 🔵 round shape, 6cm radius, 1cm thick
- 🔵 each uncooked biscuit weighing between the tolerance of 45g and 55g
- 🔵 contains 20g fat per 100g, 25g sugar per 100g and 1–5g fibre per 100g
- 🔵 packaged in twos to sell as a snack.

Biscuits

Ingredients:

300g SR flour   150g butter or margarine

150g sugar   1 egg

Method:

1 Preheat the oven to 180°C, Gas 4.

2 Cream the butter with the sugar until light and fluffy.

3 Add the egg and mix again.

4 Sieve the flour into the mixing bowl and mix in.

5 Divide the mixture into12 equal-sized pieces and roll into balls. Place onto a greased baking tray.

6 Bake for 10-15 minutes until golden brown.

7 Leave on the tray for 3 minutes before placing on to a cooling tray.

A standard product

You have seen different ways to extend a product lifecycle. You now need to experience extending a lifecycle by looking at a product then developing it so that it appeals to different people profiles. This means that more of the product will be sold and its lifecycle will be longer. Before you develop a product you need to know how to make the **standard product** and what it should be like – its **specification**.

Think about it!

PA When you have completed the FPT, evaluate the product by answering these questions.

1 **ABC** Explain how you made sure the products were all the same size and shape.

2 **ABC** Did the colour, taste and texture match the design specification? Explain how.

3 **ICT** Produce a nutritional label showing the amounts of fat, sugar and fibre in the product.

In the previous unit it was explained that you could use an attribute profile to easily show what you want a product to be like. You can also use a line drawing like **E** to explain what your product should be like.

E

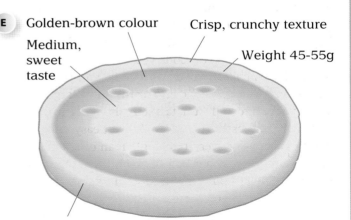

Golden-brown colour   Crisp, crunchy texture

Medium, sweet taste   Weight 45-55g

Round shape, 6cm radius, 1mm thick

25g sugar per 100g

Contains 20g fat per 100g

1–5g fibre per 100g

Packaged in twos to sell as a snack

Plenary

You have learned about people profiles and you now understand that to use people profiles you must first learn some basic making skills.

Developing a standard product

Key words

bulk   the main ingredient in a recipe

flowchart a chart showing the sequence of stages in the design and making of a food product

Once you know how to make a standard recipe, you can then think about all the different varieties you could make. You could change the recipe in all sorts of ways to match different person profiles. Look at the ideas in **A**.

Functions of ingredients

Before you produce ideas for variations you need to understand the function of each basic ingredient. For example, if you decide to develop a low-fat biscuit, you cannot just take out all the butter in the recipe; it does not work. Look at the basic ingredients used in biscuits in table **B**.

Are there any other ingredients you could add? Would these affect the outcome of the biscuit? Consider table **C** and complete it with your suggested alternative ingredients.

Ingredient added	Function	Effect
Grated apple	● Adds vitamins and NSP ● Adds moisture	● Less liquid needed
Sultanas	● Adds sweetness ● Adds NSP	● Less sugar needed

C   *Alternative ingredients for biscuit recipe*

Basic ingredient	Function	
Flour	● Forms the structure of the biscuit ● Is the **bulk** ingredient ● Contains baking powder which helps the biscuit rise ● Helps turn the biscuit brown	
Sugar	● Adds sweetness ● Makes the biscuit crunchy ● Adds to the colour	
Fat (butter or margarine)	● Adds flavour ● Makes a crunchy texture	
Eggs	● Helps bind dry ingredients ● Contains protein that helps mixtures to set	

B   *Functions of basic biscuit ingredients*

You can model your ideas by drawing annotated three-dimensional sketches of them, like the one on page 41 or the one in **D**.

D

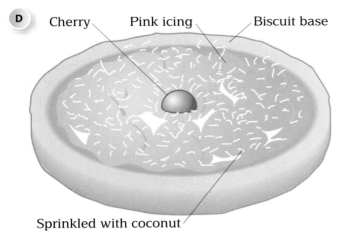

Cherry   Pink icing   Biscuit base

Sprinkled with coconut

FPT Developing products

D It's a good idea to make one or more of your ideas. This will test them and make sure they work.

Flowcharts

You also need to start writing and following detailed plans on how to make the biscuit so that each time you make it you produce the same quality biscuit – one which looks and tastes the same each time. If you write the method of making (the plan) as a **flowchart** it is easy to follow and, more importantly, it is easy to see where you have to decide if your mixture is correct.

A flowchart is a simple way of drawing a plan. It shows you where to start, what to do next and when you have to make a decision. It shows you the unit operations of the method. A flowchart is easier to follow if you use symbols for different parts.

E shows the three common symbols in a flowchart.

Name	Symbol	What it shows
Terminator	⬭	Beginning or end of the plan
Process	▭	What needs to be done
Decision	◇	A question is asked with yes or no answer

E   *Flowchart symbols*

F is an example of a flowchart for a standard biscuit showing the unit operations.

F

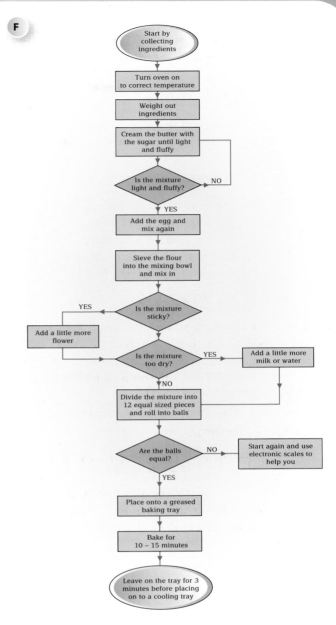

Think about it!

1 **ABC** Write a specification for the biscuit(s) you will make using the example on page 41 as a guideline.

2 **ICT** Use the flowchart **F** to help you to draw a flowchart for your chosen variety of a biscuit or other product that you are going to make. You might find it easier to do this using ICT.

Plenary

You should understand how to adapt a product successfully.

Research techniques

When you were asked to come up with some ideas for varieties of your food product, you probably found it quite difficult. Even if you think you have a good idea, how do you know it is suitable for the occasion or people you are designing for? How do you know it will sell and make a profit? If you complete some research, this will help you think of ideas and will also help you to find out if your ideas will be successful.

You have already learned about and completed several different kinds of research.

- Evaluating a product – looking at a product and its packaging, then tasting it (sensory evaluation).
- Experimenting and modelling with ingredients – using small quantities to make more than one variety at a time.
- Asking people questions – the questions have to be planned out carefully so that they are relevant and you get the right information from them.

Let us think about other ways to research.

Mindmapping

This is a **mindmapping** exercise to sell more carrots. Here are the facts. Sales of carrots are falling and carrot growers are getting worried. They have employed you to come up with some outrageous ideas that might help increase sales of carrots to manufacturers. What about carrot and chocolate spread or cheese and carrot burgers? You might think that some of the ideas you come up with would never work, but imagine what people said when someone came up with the idea of a mars bar ice cream or a baked bean pizza!

This method of research is often called mindmapping. You could mindmap all the extra ingredients that could be used to make varieties of biscuits.

A

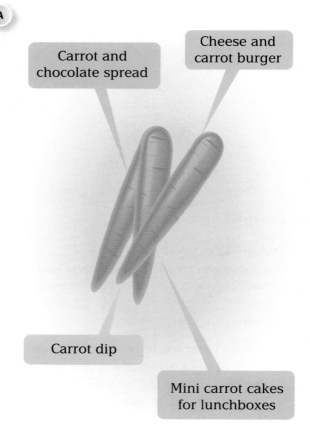

Carrot and chocolate spread

Cheese and carrot burger

Carrot dip

Mini carrot cakes for lunchboxes

Evaluating

Looking at existing products (a shop survey) is another way to collect information and is a method of evaluation. You can gain lots of useful information by just looking at the variety of one product. You might

B   *A range of biscuits*

find out that there are not enough fruity biscuits so you could concentrate on ideas for biscuits with different fruits. You might find out there is very little choice of large biscuits to put into snack boxes.

Some of you may find it difficult to go to a supermarket, but even going to a small local shop will give you some ideas. You could also look in recipe books for ideas or use the Internet to search for biscuit recipes, look at lists of biscuits at online shopping sites or look at the website for the manufacturer of the particular product.

Sketching

Designers use sketchbooks and folios to record thoughts and design ideas. Similarly a person who is developing (or designing) a new food product will record their ideas and thoughts in some way, perhaps in a sketchbook. You have learned how to sketch ideas. If you use sketches, you can easily show other people what you are thinking. But you must annotate your sketches (label and explain) to show what the drawing means.

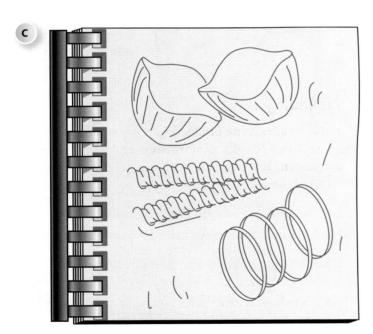

Mood-boards

Designers also use mood-boards and collages that include inspiring photos and pictures. Mood-boards might be collections of pictures or photos that illustrate a particular country and its foods or a particular occasion such as Easter. **D** is an example

from Year 10 students studying Food Technology at Beauchamp College in Leicestershire and is an example of a mood-board about Pakistani food.

Analysis

Good research means that you find out details and information about your chosen product. You use a number of sources for the research and then you will be able to analyse the results. Analysis means collecting all the results together and deciding just what has been discovered. After this is done, you will be able to design your product for a particular purpose or person profile.

Think about it!

TS Can you carry out an analysis of a product and make an even better one? If you are making this next new product, don't forget to write another new specification so that you will be able to evaluate it after it has been made.

Plenary

You have learned about all the different kinds of research that can be carried out to help you design a product.

Quality controls

Objectives

In this lesson you will learn how the use of quality controls ensures quality standard products.

Quality counts!

If you are going to make a product again and again you need to make sure you keep on making the same quality product. Quality in food is important for food manufacturers. The food has to be safe to eat and taste good if customers are going to buy the food again. When you are making food at school or at home you might sometimes forget to season food with salt and pepper. You could just think, 'I'll try to remember to add some next time I make it'. But if you are selling lots of food products and one batch is not quite right, customers will start to buy another brand straight away because it was not as good as usual. Food manufacturers, big or small, do not usually get a second chance!

Accuracy

Writing a detailed plan or flowchart on how to make a product is one way to help ensure the quality of the product, but you need to use other ways to help you too.

Cliff Cowman uses his skill to divide up sausages to the right size. He aims to make his sausages to a certain size so that fourteen sausages weigh a kilo. It took several years of practice for Cliff to be able to divide the sausages up accurately without regularly weighing them. Cliff's shop also makes several varieties of burgers. A simple device is used to measure out the correct amount of burger meat – an ice cream scoop! Scales are used occasionally to check that the weight of the burgers is within five grams of the correct weight.

Farmhouse Biscuits use various methods to ensure the same quality biscuits are made. The biscuit must always taste the same, so accurate scales are used to weigh out all the ingredients. See photo **B**. The temperature of the convector ovens is controlled and

A

The correct amount of burger-meat must be measured out each time

the baking of biscuits is timed. Of course the biscuits are checked to ensure they are the same size, weight and appearance. Equal-sized biscuits are very important, so moulds are used for some biscuits and extruders for others. An extruder machine forces out the biscuit mixture, while a computer works out when the correct amount needs to be cut off with a thin wire.

B *Accurate scales are used to weigh the ingredients exactly*

Quality control checks also take place during the process of making each biscuit.

- Uncooked biscuits are weighed to check that the extruder or moulds are actually producing the right weight biscuit.
- Cooked biscuits are also checked for weight, also colour, size and height.
- Every batch of biscuits is tasted for flavour and texture (crispiness and crunch).
- Finally the packets of biscuits are checked for weight (see picture **C**).

C The finished packets are checked to make sure they are the correct weight

Quality control

The use of computers, moulds and quality controls are very important in the food industry to make sure customers buy products again and again. So what can be used in the Food Technology classroom to ensure quality control? There are many pieces of equipment that can be used to help maintain quality.

- Food mixers and processors that can set to run for a length of time and to keep the same speed over that time, or the same sized grater may be used for appropriate ingredients.
- Simple rolling guides/spacers for the same and even thickness.
- Cutters, moulds or special moulded tins.
- Electronic scales.
- Oven thermometers and timers.

D An example of a conveyor oven for a Food Technology room

A Food Technology room may also have a small conveyor (tunnel) oven which will make sure products are cooked much more accurately than a domestic oven for the same time and temperature (see **D**). This oven works exactly the same way as those used in food factories but is a much smaller version. There are two temperatures to set and control: the top temperature and the bottom temperature. These can either be the same or different depending on the product. Often the bottom temperature is lower because the product is closer to the heat source. The speed of the conveyor belt controls how long the products are in the oven and therefore how long they are cooked for. Both the temperatures and the speed have to be correct for each product, as you cannot get the product out of the middle of the oven if you think it looks done! More importantly, the product has to be exactly the same each time so quality control is paramount!

D Cutters, moulds and moulded tins are used to ensure each product is the correct size and weight

Think about it!

TS **ABC** Quality controls are about taste, weight, shape, time, temperature and hygiene. List the quality controls that need to happen when making the following food products:

- pizza
- a cheese sandwich
- burgers
- a milk shake.

Plenary

You should be able to identify different quality controls which can be used while making food products.

Using quality controls and costing a product

Objectives

In this lesson you will learn how to use quality controls.

You should have already written a flowchart for your product to make sure the process of making is the same each time. Now quality controls need to be added to the table so that you, or anyone else, can produce high-quality products in quantity. Here is the basic recipe and specification again, but this time some suggestions are included to make sure the quality remains the same each time.

Specification for biscuits

- golden-brown colour
- crisp, crunchy texture
- medium-sweet taste
- round shape, 6cm radius, 1cm thick
- each cooked biscuit weighing between the tolerance of 45g and 55g
- contains 20g fat per 100g, 25g sugar per 100g and 1–5g fibre per 100g
- packaged in twos to sell as a snack.

Now use the information in **A**, and the information on pages 46–7 to rewrite your flowchart for an adapted biscuit to include all the quality control checks that need to be carried out. You might want to do it like table **C**.

A

Biscuits

Ingredients:

200g self raising flour   150g sugar

150g Butter or margarine   1 egg (110g)

Method:

1. Preheat the oven to 180C/ Gas 4. Use an oven thermometer to check.
2. Cream the butter with the sugar until light and fluffy. What does this mean? Time it. Use equipment to help.
3. Add the egg and mix again.
4. Sieve the flour into the mixing bowl and mix in.
5. Divide the mixture into 12 equal sized pieces and roll into balls. How equal? Use cutters, scales or a mould.
6. Place onto a greased baking tray.
7. Bake for 10 –15 minutes until golden brown. What is golden brown?

Costing a product

Which product would you buy – the most expensive or the cheapest? Is there a difference between products of different costs? Is it flavour, size, appearance or quality of ingredients which is different, and does it matter?

How would you be able to tell which is the better biscuit in **B**? You could just decide that the more expensive biscuit was the better one. Or you could carry out some sensory evaluation yourself or by asking others to taste and give their opinion.

B

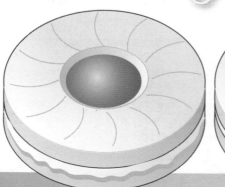

An expensive biscuit

A cheaper biscuit

Method/process	What could go wrong	Quality control
Collect ingredients	Poor quality ingredients – eggs past sell-by date	Check date, buy from reliable suppliers
Measure out ingredients	Incorrect weighing	Use computerized scales
Turn on oven	Incorrect temperature	Use oven thermometer
Cream fat and sugar until light and fluffy	Not light enough, not enough air added	Use electric whisk on high for three minutes
Add egg and mix	Not sufficiently well mixed together	Use electric whisk on medium for one minute
Sieve flour into mixture and mix	Flour still visible, or beaten too much	Use electric whisk on low for one minute
Divide mixture into twelve portions	Portions not equal sized	Use mould to shape or electronic scales
Place on baking tray	They could stick to tray	Grease tray
Bake for 10–15 minutes	Undercooked, burnt	Use timer, check temperature, check colour
Leave on tray for three minutes	Biscuits not set so could break up	Use timer

C *Quality control checks*

The spreadsheet in **D** shows the ingredients used in the standard biscuit made during the FPT. You will need to find out from a shop or supermarket the price of both sets of ingredients you are using – the standard ingredients and the value or cheap ingredients. Cost both products and then make a comparison between them. Carry out some sensory evaluation testing asking other people to give their opinions about the two products. Record:

- the products you made
- how the ingredients differed, apart from cost, if at all
- what were the differences between the completed products? Comment on appearance, flavour and cost. You could do this using the digital images and sensory evaluation charts.

Ingredient	Bought weight (g)	Price	Amount used (g)	Cost
SR flour	1500		200	
white sugar	1000		150	
butter	250		150	
egg	6		1	
			Total cost	

D *Use a spreadsheet to cost your product*

FPT Choosing ingredients

Let us take a look at working with some ingredients so that we are able to make a more informed choice about choosing ingredients and developing new products using them. Working with a partner, decide upon an investigation you could carry out or follow your teacher's suggestion for a product you could make. It could be a biscuit, cake, burger or any of the other products you have made during Food Technology lessons. Using the information you have learned about planning and flow charts, organize your lesson to make the two similar products, one using standard ingredients the other using value or cheap ingredients. One person should use all standard ingredients. Record the outcomes from the investigation using a digital camera. In order to cost the product use a spreadsheet set out in a similar way to the one in **D**.

Spreadsheets

D A spreadsheet is a useful tool for modelling products. In this unit you have looked at the cost of the two products as they are being developed. It is possible to change amounts and types of ingredients and see how this changes the cost of the outcome? Remember though, as before, if you intend to change, reduce or increase ingredients it should be for something similar e.g. change Edam cheese for Cheddar cheese. Most importantly the functions of the ingredients should be considered and the recipe must be tested as a prototype.

Plenary
You should be able to use quality controls to make biscuits in quantity to a high standard.

Temperature control

Objectives

In this lesson you will learn to understand temperature, time controls and high-risk foods.

Key words

hazard anything that has the potential to cause harm to the consumer

Think about it!

True or false?

1 All foods contain bacteria.

2 All bacteria is harmful.

3 You are more likely to get food poisoning from a ham sandwich than a jam sandwich.

4 Frozen foods contain only dead bacteria.

5 If a beefburger is brown on the outside it is cooked.

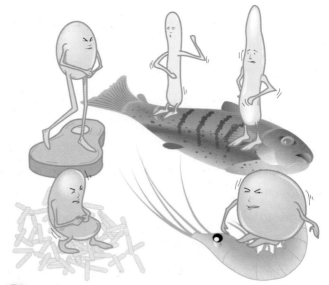

A Bacteria at room temperature

High-risk foods have a high protein and moisture content and if not stored correctly provide ideal conditions for bacterial growth. If you want to beat the bacteria team (see pages 18–19) you have to be especially careful with these foods. Look at them again in **A** and at the list of high-risk foods below.

- Raw meat and fish
- Dairy products
- Cooked meat and poultry
- Shellfish and seafood
- Gravies, sauces, stocks, soups and stews
- Egg products e.g. raw egg in chilled desserts and mayonnaise
- Cooked rice
- Protein-based baby foods

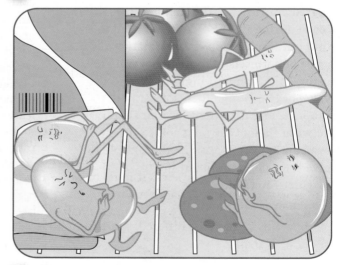

B Bacteria dormant (sleeping) in a fridge

These foods must be covered and stored in a fridge at all times. Any that are raw must be thoroughly cooked so any bacteria are destroyed. Remember bacteria need warmth to grow. The best temperature for growth is 37°C (body temperature). Even at room temperature, about 24°C, there is a danger, so high-risk foods cannot stay at this temperature for long. We know these foods should be stored in a fridge, below 5°C, because bacteria become dormant in cold temperatures and hardly grow at all. If food is frozen at between –18°C and –29°C, bacteria are in a deep sleep. They do not grow, but they are still there.

Bacteria cannot survive hot temperatures. At a temperature of 63°C or above they are all dead. To make sure that food is safe to eat and that all bacteria have been destroyed, food has to be cooked to above 75°C. It has to be piping hot, even in the middle. The temperature of all food which is cooked in canteens, restaurants and factories must be checked regularly using temperature probes and records must be kept showing when they have been used and the temperature recorded.

C

Food is safe if it is either cold or very hot. If food is warm it's in the danger zone (see **D**). When food has been cooked it must be eaten straight away. If not, the food must be cooled quickly, then stored at a cold temperature. If hot food is put into a fridge the temperature of the fridge rises above 5°C and allows bacteria to grow. Nevertheless it must be put in the fridge within one and a half hours of cooking so it needs to be cooled quickly. In one and a half hours,

one bacterium would multiply into twenty-four bacteria. If you left that food out overnight, one bacterium would multiply into 250 million bacteria. In food factories, blast chillers are used to quickly chill food to between 0°C and 2°C.

If food is warm it could be a **hazard**. A hazard is anything that may cause harm to someone. When you work with food you must think about possible hazards and how to prevent them. Look at the chart in **E** for making Bolognaise sauce. It shows some possible hygiene hazards and how temperature and time controls can prevent hazards.

D

The danger zone: bacteria can grow at temperatures between 5°C and 63°C

Think about it!

1   Write out a chart like **E** for making a lasagne, a burger in a bun, and a roast chicken.
2   Work out the possible hygiene hazards and how you would stop them happening.

Plenary

You have learned about high-risk foods that must be kept out of the danger zone.

Method	Possible hazard	Temperature and time control
Collect ingredients	Warm ingredients	Store below 5°C
Sweat onions		
Fry meat until brown		
Add all other ingredients		
Cook until soft	Not hot enough	Cook long enough for centre to be above 75°C
Cool	Kept warm for too long	Cool quickly for one and a half hours only and put in fridge
Store overnight	Kept warm	Store in fridge below 5°C
Heat up	Not hot enough	Heat up until middle is above 75°C
Serve		Serve immediately

E   *Bolognaise sauce: possible hazards and ways to avoid them*

Starchy foods

Objectives

In this lesson you will find out about starchy and staple foods.

Key words

staple foods	the main parts of a person's diet
sauce	a liquid or semi-solid accompaniment to a meal
bland	tasteless

Pasta, rice, noodles and potatoes all have something in common. They are classified as starchy foods and they all come from plants. We need starchy foods to give us energy and to fill us up. A little protein is also found in these foods.

Starchy foods come in different shapes and sizes, have their own texture and flavour, and can be bought and cooked in different ways. See how many more examples you could add to the spider diagram **A**.

Starchy foods can be cooked in different ways or flavoured so they taste different. For example, shops and supermarkets have various flavours of mashed potatoes to tempt consumers.

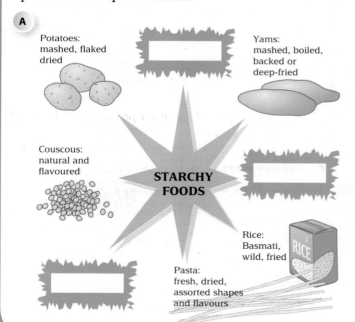

A

Potatoes: mashed, flaked dried

Yams: mashed, boiled, backed or deep-fried

Couscous: natural and flavoured

STARCHY FOODS

Rice: Basmati, wild, fried

Pasta: fresh, dried, assorted shapes and flavours

FPT Starchy foods

1   Perhaps you could try adding finely-grated cheese, bacon pieces or mustard to plain mashed potatoes. What kinds of ingredients could you add to the potatoes while they are cooking? What about chopped onion? Record what you find, commenting on flavour, appearance and texture and making a comparison between the types.

2   Look at the starchy foods in **B**, which are prepared, cooked and ready to eat.

  a)   FPT Find out how to prepare and cook each of these staple foods.

  b)   Describe the appearance, texture and flavour of each. You may have the opportunity to taste each of them, and record your findings as an attribute profile. Use these sensory descriptors on the profile – white, soft, grainy, bland, lumpy, tasty, spicy.

  c)   Explain your conclusions from this investigation. What did you think? Are they all a little tasteless or bland when they are eaten on their own?

B

cooked rice

mashed potato

couscous

cooked pasta

When starch is heated in water the starch grains swell and at about 100°C they gelatinise. Sauces are thickened by this gelatinisation of starch. You will find out more about this later.

Think about it!

1   ABC Can you remember why we should eat starchy foods?

2   ABC Discuss with another person in your group other examples of staple foods of particular countries, and record your findings.

Benefits of starchy foods

Starchy foods are the best way to obtain energy, better than eating lots of sugar and fat. Think about the balanced plate (see pages 10–11). Most starchy foods have the added bonus of containing vitamins, minerals and NSP. Another benefit is that they are cheap. There is a big difference in price between starchy foods and most other foods and certainly a difference in the amounts and types of nutrients they supply.

Starchy foods can be **bland** – lacking in flavour. Many ready-prepared meals contain starchy foods and because food manufacturers want to tempt us to buy their products they add flavour, colour, texture and some other nutrients to the starchy food usually in the form of a **sauce**.

The food products shown in **D** are only a few examples of ready meals containing a starchy food and a sauce and have been manufactured to attract a particular group of consumers.

D

Nutritional information	White bread	Cheddar cheese
Typical values	400g loaf	400g
Energy	4032kJ	6800kJ
	1132kcal	1640kcal
Protein	33.2g	100g
Carbohydrate	189.2g	0.4g
of which sugars	13.6g	0.4g
Fat	6.8g	137.6g
of which saturates	2.4g	86.8g
of which mono-saturates	3.2g	37.6g
of which polyunsaturates	1.2g	5.6g
Fibre	10.4g	0.0g
Sodium	1.6g	2.8g

C   A nutritional chart comparing the values of 400g of white bread and 400g of cheddar cheese

What is a staple food?

Staple foods usually form the largest part of a meal. Different countries are well known and celebrated for their staple foods. For example, China's staple food is rice, while Italy's is pasta.

Think about it!

1. 123 Compare the price and the nutritional value of a small loaf of white bread (400g) with 400g of cheddar cheese by looking at the nutritional table in **C**.

2. Study the information on the labels in **D** carefully before answering these questions about the products. Devise your own charts to record your findings.

   a) ABC Which part of the meal, the starchy food or the sauce, do you think forms the bigger part?

   b) Consider each of the meals in turn and then identify the type of person or group of people each is aimed at. Describe how well you think the product meets its intended need.

   c) Identify the protein foods and the starchy foods that are included.

   d) Choose two of the ready-prepared meals and write down what you think the manufacturers' design criteria were.

Plenary

You should know why starchy foods and staple foods are important. You have carried out investigations with a variety of starchy foods and are able to describe the sensory properties of some starchy foods. You have learned how food manufacturers make starchy foods more interesting.

Sauces

A definition of a sauce could be, 'liquid seasoning for food'. Sauces add flavour, colour and texture to a food product. They can be added as an extra to a meal, for example apple sauce with roast pork, or mixed in with the meal, for example macaroni cheese.

Sauces can be classified by the way they are thickened:

- with egg such as mayonnaise, hollandaise and custard
- with vegetable or fruit purees such as tomato sauce and apple sauce
- with starch, these can be white or brown

Sauces can also be made by combining two thickening methods, such as a bolognaise sauce that can be thickened with starch and tomato puree. By far the most important and most popular way to thicken sauces is using starch.

White sauce

There are three ways to make a white sauce.

The blended method

This is when starch (usually cornflour) is mixed with a liquid and stirred over heat until it gelatinises (thickens).

Advantages:

- a quick method of making a sauce
- it is a fat-free sauce – ideal to use if making a low-fat dish.

Disadvantage:

- it makes a bland-tasting sauce as there is no fat to add flavour.

The all-in-one method

This is when starch (usually wheatflour) and fat are mixed with liquid and whisked over heat until it gelatinises. It is called **all-in-one** as all the ingredients are put in the saucepan together and cooked.

Advantage:

- this sauce is easy to make if constantly stirred during heating with a balloon whisk.

Disadvantage:

- the sauce may taste of flour.

The roux method

This is when fat is melted, flour is added, mixed into the fat and cooked for one or two minutes. This is called the **roux**. Liquid is slowly mixed into the roux and this mixture is stirred over heat until it gelatinises.

Advantage:

- it makes a tasty sauce and is the method used by professional chefs.

Disadvantages:

- it is more difficult to make without getting lumps in it
- it takes longer to make than the other sauces mentioned.

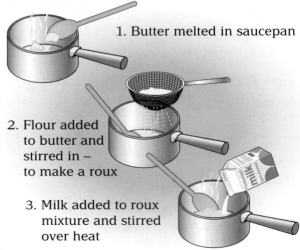

1. Butter melted in saucepan

2. Flour added to butter and stirred in – to make a roux

3. Milk added to roux mixture and stirred over heat

A *The roux method of making white sauce*

Brown sauce

A brown sauce is traditionally made in the same way as a white sauce. The roux is cooked for longer until it turns golden brown. Brown stock (made from red meat) is added to the roux and heated until it gelatinises. The flavour in this sauce comes from the stock that has been boiled up for hours. An easier and quicker way to make a brown sauce is one that starts out with a 'sweated' onion. Other vegetables are added and cooked or meat is added and browned. Then flour is stirred in with other seasonings and liquid is added (water, stock, tomato juice or even coconut milk). This mixture is stirred over heat until the liquid has gelatinised and simmered (cooked over a low heat) until all the ingredients are soft and tender.

Professional chefs sweat onions using the following method:

● Add a little oil to a saucepan.

● Heat the oil up.

● Add chopped onions to the pan and stir them, immediately turning the heat down to low.

● Put a lid on the pan and leave it to sweat for ten minutes. The pan lid is vital so the steam produced does not escape! Sweating the onions makes them very soft and sweet, they 'melt' into the other ingredients and don't remain stringy and chewy.

Many sauces are made in this way such as bolognaise sauce, chilli sauce, curry and sweet and sour sauce.

Hollandaise sauce

Sauces thickened with egg are rich in flavour. Egg sets at a certain temperature and will thicken the other ingredients. Hot sauces made with egg are difficult to make as it is easy to 'curdle' the mixture if it is overheated: the sauce will separate and look bitty.

Fruit or vegetable puree sauces

Sauces thickened with vegetables or fruit purees are healthy because they contain a variety of vitamins and minerals and also NSP (fibre). Vegetables and fruit often help to thicken brown sauces. For example the tomatoes added to a bolognaise sauce help to thicken it. Some pureed sauces have starch added to make them thicker.

Smart starches

Key words

waxy maize starch	starch that remains runny when cold
modified starch	starch that has been developed chemically so that it forms a gel with cold water or milk
genetically modified	food biologically changed in some way, for example, to give a higher nutritional value in rice, to make plants more resistant to pests or to make animals grow faster

What is a smart food?

A smart food is one that has been changed from its natural state so that it behaves in a particular way. These changes can be physical or chemical. Let us look at smart starches which are used by food manufacturers to thicken sauces. Ordinary cornflour and wheatflour have disadvantages in that they do not behave as required in certain situations. When a sauce is made with cornflour or wheatflour it is stirred with a spoon or whisk over the heat until it thickens (gelatinises) into a smooth sauce. When it cools down it sets into a gel like a blancmange.

When it is reheated it usually changes back into a smooth sauce if you stir it and if it hasn't been stored in a fridge for longer than a day. The longer it is kept, the more difficult it becomes to make it into a smooth sauce again.

Look at the blancmange in **A**. If the blancmange is frozen and then defrosted it becomes quite difficult to get it back to a smooth texture as the sauce separates into solid and liquid when it is defrosted (see photo **B**).

Food manufacturers who produce chilled and frozen foods with sauces have problems using ordinary cornflour and wheatflour because of this reaction. In the 1940s, food manufacturers started to produce more packaged instant foods such as fruit desserts. Starch was in demand to thicken these food products.

Around this time a new starch was discovered called **waxy maize starch**. It is called 'waxy' because when you cut open the grain it has a shiny waxy surface. This starch was used in these products because it behaves in a different way to normal maize starch (cornflour). It does not set into a gel when cold. It stays runny (viscous). It still has some disadvantages, because although it is runny, the texture can be sticky rather than smooth.

Modified starch

As frozen and chilled meals and other processed foods became more popular, food manufacturers had to make improvements and find better thickeners to

A

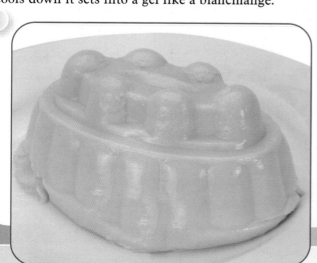

B

use. Food scientists began to find ways to modify (change) starches either physically or chemically to:

- stop sauce breakdown (separation into solid and liquid)
- stop them losing their viscosity (thickness) when extra ingredients are added (lemon juice, sugar)
- stop them losing their viscosity (thickness) when mixed vigorously during processing.

Starches are modified to overcome problems in food manufacturing: to make them easier to use, more stable in processing and to give a wider range of textures.

There are more than 100 **modified starches** available to food manufacturers. These starches are not available to buy in shops and supermarkets, but there are some specialist starches which are generally available such as a sauce flour (see photo **C**). This is a fine powder made using special milling techniques and can be added directly to hot liquids to thicken them. This starch has been physically modified. Thickening granules are made from physically modified potato starch and can also be added directly to hot sauces to thicken without lumps forming.

(FPT) *Modified starch*

Use at least one modified starch to make a sauce. When it is made, chill half of it and freeze the other half. Explain any changes in its viscosity (defrost the frozen sample first). Otherwise, think about the changes that would take place in the sauce if cornflour or modified maize starch are used.

You may have the opportunity to carry out a group experiment with a chemically modified starch and ordinary cornflour. Add sugar and lemon juice to each and compare the results. Use an electric mixer to mix vigorously and compare them again.

C *Sauce flour is an example of a specialist starch that can be bought in the shops*

Think about it!

1 Look at the products and their labels in **D**. They all use modified starches to thicken sauces.

Explain what these products would be like if ordinary cornflour or wheatflour were used.

D

2 (CT) The word modified can be confused with the term **genetically modified**. Find out what genetically modified means, record your findings and explain what you think are the advantages and disadvantages of these foods.

Plenary

The information on these pages will make you more aware of the different smart starches which are used in foods. It should make you think about the foods you are eating.

More smart foods

Key words

organoleptic properties	properties of a food that can be described during sensory analysis (tasting)
extruded	forced through a die or nozzle under pressure
unit operations	stages in the production process
manufacturing specification	a detailed production plan including every detail that a manufacturer needs to make a product again and again

Meat analogues

Meat analogues are ingredients that mimic the **organoleptic properties** (taste, texture and appearance) of meat. These meat analogues use natural ingredients such as soya beans and Quorn™. They are changed during the manufacturing process so that they look, taste and feel like meat. They are an alternative to meat.

Textured Vegetable Protein (TVP) and Quorn™

TVP is made from bundles of **extruded** soya protein. Plain TVP may taste 'beany' so it needs to be flavoured. There are several flavoured TVP products available. Quorn™ is a mycoprotein. An organism called *Fusarium graminearum*, a relative of the mushroom, is fermented to produce fine fibres. These are formed into mince, chunks and cutlets.

FPT Using meat analogues

D Try making a brown sauce such as a bolognaise sauce using a meat analogue.

Functional foods

Functional foods are foods that contain an ingredient that gives health promoting properties.

- Benecol products, including margarine and yoghurt, contain parts of plants that can stop cholesterol being absorbed into the body.
- Omega-3 eggs contain Omega-3 fatty acids normally found in fatty fish. Hens are fed on a diet rich in Omega-3 fatty acids so that eating their eggs passes on these fatty acids, which are good for the heart.
- Yakult contains live 'good' bacteria that are thought to improve the health of the bowel.
- Encapsulated technology is when microscopic capsules are used to add extras to a product. The capsule breaks open during eating to release the central ingredient such as a nutrient or a flavour. Some sports bars are fortified with encapsulated nutrients.

Think about it!

1 **ABC** Carry out some research on other meat analogues by looking at the products available in a supermarket.

2 **ICT** Use the following link to find out about Tivall: www.heinemann.co.uk/hotlinks. Can you explain why it is not as popular as Quorn™?

3 Write a list of other fortified foods which can be found in shops and supermarkets.

4 **123** Half a dozen 'value' eggs can cost as little as 25 pence. Half a dozen eggs fortified with Omega-3 fatty acids cost over £1. Write a report explaining the advantages and disadvantages of each kind of egg.

A

More starchy foods B

Starchy foods are usually combined with a sauce to make them more exciting. Often, protein foods, seasonings and vegetables are added for more interest and to make a complete meal. Numerous products can be developed by combining ingredients in different ways. Look at the suggestions for ready-prepared meal ingredients and how they might be combined in **B**.

Diagram B:

- PASTA — Fresh, Dried, Different shapes, ?
- SAUCE — spicy, Cheese, Onion, ?
- SEASONINGS — Salt, Basil, Cummin, ?
- POTATOES — Mashed, Boiled, Jacket, ?
- PROTEIN FOOD — Minced beef, lentils, Chicken, Tuna, Onion, ?
- RICE — Basmati, Long grain
- VEGETABLES — Carrot, Onion, Broccoli

Think about it!

1 D Add as many more suggestions as you can to the different sections of diagram **B**.

2 D Consider which ingredients you could put together to make different products. Take three different starchy foods in turn and suggest a sauce, seasoning, protein food and vegetable to complement it. Look at the example in **C**: fresh pasta (starchy food), white cheese sauce (sauce), salt (seasoning), chicken (protein), broccoli and onion (vegetables).

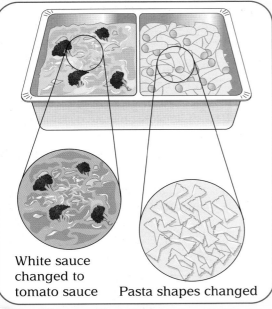

White sauce changed to tomato sauce   Pasta shapes changed

C *Chicken and broccoli with pasta: how many different ways can you think of to alter this recipe?*

The diagram in **C** also shows ways to develop your ideas by changing one or two of the components each time. Perhaps you could try out this technique here? Imagine you are going to make one of the food products you have suggested here. You would have to decide upon and then organise the order in which you would prepare it – these steps are called **unit operations** and are a list, a plan or a flow chart of how to make the product. Remember that some tasks need to be carried out before others such as the food which takes the longest to prepare or cook needs to be started first – in this case the chicken.

FPT Combining ingredients

D Choose one of your ideas and decide how you would make it. Put together a flowchart of the unit operations including quality and hygiene controls you need to carry out before you begin. Look back at chart **E** on page 51. Now you may have time to try out your instructions. One thing to consider, especially if you are a food manufacturer is how to get the product exactly the same each time it is made. Some things are easy, for example, the same size, shape and type of pasta can be used, but with other ingredients it takes more thought.

Quality control

Food manufacturers use a very accurate recipe called a **manufacturing specification**. Instead of chopping up and using '1 onion', the onion will be chopped to a certain size and there will be a specified amount: '150g chopped onion, pieces <3cm'. In the same way, the variety of onion may be detailed, especially if it is a particular type such as a 'red onion'. Write down an accurate manufacturing specification for a product you have made.

Plenary

You should be aware of smart foods that can be bought and used in food products other than sauces. You should be able to plan a flowchart showing unit operations and some controls.

Introducing systems

A factory is organized to make sure everything runs smoothly. Let us look at a simple example of how a factory producing spaghetti bolognaise (a starchy food with a sauce) would be organized.

Systems

There are three important parts in the production, or making, of any product – input, process and output. This is referred to as a **system**. Table **A** shows some examples to explain a basic system.

Factory-produced spaghetti bolognaise would be made in three main parts. The **inputs** are prepared first. These are meat sauce, spaghetti and cheese. Remember the input stage involves the storage of the different ingredients before they are processed (the second part) and then combined as the finished product (the third part). In this case, the meat sauce is prepared and made, the pasta is freshly made and the cheese grated. The product is then assembled and packaged to produce the **output**.

If it goes wrong!

What happens if something goes wrong – too much pasta is added or not enough bolognaise sauce is deposited? At regular intervals some products will be checked making sure they meet the manufacturing specification. If something is going wrong, machinery will be adjusted and the problem will be solved (feedback).

Quantities

The quantities of ingredients and the equipment used in industry differ from Food Technology lessons or making food at home. Instead of just making enough spaghetti bolognaise for three or four people, a factory will make enough for hundreds of shops and supermarkets, perhaps thousands of portions in one day. Large vats are used for the large quantities.

Quality

In a similar way, industry does not employ lots of people to weigh and measure the sauce or cheese into the correct amount for each portion. A machine or depositor does this job efficiently and quickly. The product is being made for thousands of consumers so it is very important to check that the system includes hygiene, quality and time controls. Imagine the problems if someone developed food poisoning! The system is very carefully planned and monitored so it does not go wrong.

Type of system	Digestive system	Scone production system	Cheese sandwich production system	Your example
Input	Food	Flour, fat, milk, sugar	Sliced bread, spread, grated cheese	
Process	Digestion	Weighing, cutting, kneading, rolling, baking	Slicing bread, combining, spreading	
Output	Energy	Plain scones	Cheese sandwich	

A Examples of basic systems

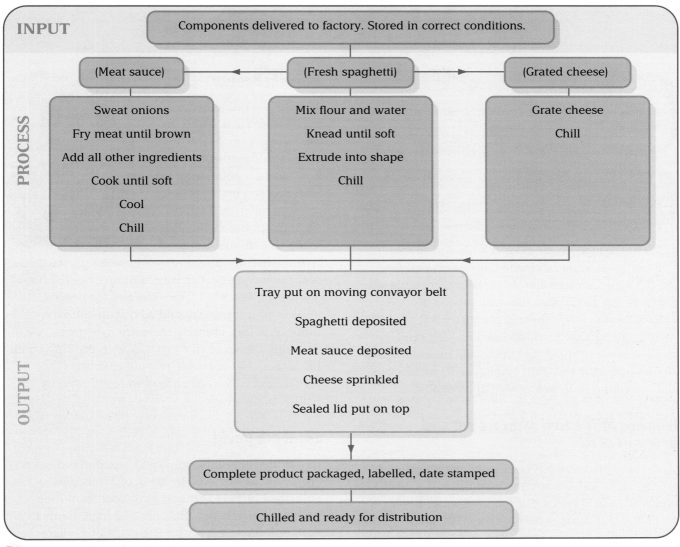

INPUT — Components delivered to factory. Stored in correct conditions.

PROCESS

(Meat sauce) — (Fresh spaghetti) — (Grated cheese)

Sweat onions
Fry meat until brown
Add all other ingredients
Cook until soft
Cool
Chill

Mix flour and water
Knead until soft
Extrude into shape
Chill

Grate cheese
Chill

OUTPUT

Tray put on moving convayor belt
Spaghetti deposited
Meat sauce deposited
Cheese sprinkled
Sealed lid put on top

Complete product packaged, labelled, date stamped

Chilled and ready for distribution

B *The production of spaghetti bolognaise*

Think about it!

1 **ABC** Look carefully at the system in **B** and then, on your own copy, indicate where there would be hygiene, quality and temperature controls (h, q, t).

2 **D** **ABC** Now use the same idea of drawing a system to describe how the production of a product you have made would be organized.

3 **FPT** You could simulate a production line to see how a dish could be made in large quantities.

Plenary

You should understand how a system for making a food product is organized in industry to make sure that it runs smoothly and there are no hazards.

Celebrity chefs 1

Much of the food we eat today is a mass-produced commodity. It could be claimed, therefore, that food items bought in shops and supermarkets are designed products that go through the same process of development as any industrial product. Food products such as pre-packaged sandwiches, breakfast cereals, cooking sauces, chilled ready-prepared meals and pasta all need the same research, development, engineering and marketing skills as a new computer game.

Who has influenced what we eat and how we eat it?

Over the years there has been a change in styles of eating. Early last century the long hours of preparation and cooking of food made the whole process into a chore, whereas nowadays most cooking is for fun, for relaxation and for pleasure.

What we eat describes who we are and the culture and age in which we live. This is particularly true if you consider the diets of people who are older or younger than you are. It is interesting to ask people in their twenties, thirties, forties, fifties and above what they think are the people or occasions which have influenced food fashions and trends. Is it true, for example, that the young people of today eat McDonalds hamburgers and drink Coca Cola because they are seen as fashionable? Or is it because they are heavily advertised by the media so young people feel pressured into consuming them? Consider the following food designers (chefs) and how their styles may have set a precedent for their times. Only a small selection has been included here and you may want to research others.

Isabella Beeton A

Mrs Beeton published her *Book of Household Management* in 1861 as a guide for Victorian women on how to run a household. It included two main sections: one on how to deal with servants (footmen, maids and so on) and another on food, recommending in great detail how to buy, select, prepare and cook food. It became an essential book not just for specific recipes but also for general household information and advice on culinary techniques. For example there are four pages describing types of rice together with cooking notes. For almost 100 years her recommendations for preparation and cooking food were followed by British housewives.

Elizabeth David

In her lifetime Elizabeth David transformed the way people ate in Britain. Her book of *Mediterranean Food* published in 1951 inspired a cookery revolution, bringing entirely new flavours and ingredients to a dull, uninteresting, post-war British diet where rationing was still a big factor. If you are not familiar with pre-war British attitudes to food and cooking, carry out some research to find out what it was like. *Mediterranean Food* started a transformation of taste and food began to be seen as a matter of fashion rather than a necessity. Elizabeth David's use of peppers, aubergines, honey and fresh herbs was inspired by her visits to countries around the Mediterranean and even further afield.

Fanny Craddock

Together with her husband, Johnny, Fanny Craddock was among the first of a new breed of television cooks who emerged during the 1960s. Fanny tended to wear fur stoles, low necklines and jewellery. The dishes she made were larger-than-life, many were brightly-coloured, rich in cream and over decorated (imitation flowers, piped mayonnaise and so on). She based many of her recipes around *Larousse Gastronomique*, the French cooking encyclopaedia. However tastes changed during the 1960s and her style of cooking quickly went out of fashion.

Madhur Jaffrey and Ken Hom

These television cooks made the British public realise that the 'ethnic' dishes which they bought from take-aways, such as sweet and sour pork and chicken tikka masala, were not authentic and had been created purely for the British palate. Madhur Jaffrey is one of the best-known authorities on Indian food. She has written a number of books explaining exactly how to achieve subtle and authentic Indian flavours. She suggests that spices are the common thread in all varieties of Indian foods, but that not all Indian food is hot and spicy. Spices are used whole, fried, roasted or ground into a paste. The information in her books explains how to combine dishes, use spices and develop dishes with Indian flavours. In a similar way, Ken Hom has managed to demystify the art of Chinese cuisine. He introduced healthy, authentic Chinese dishes such as Szechuan stir fried vegetables with noodles. His influence has been so strong that at least 50 per cent of British homes own a wok!

Delia Smith

Delia could probably appear twice in this section, firstly as a television cook who first appeared in the early 1980s, and secondly as a 'saviour' of cooking from the late 1990s onwards. Her current concern is that people may be losing the ability to enjoy preparing and cooking food and may be relying too much on ready-prepared meals, fast food and 'ping' cuisine. Her recent books and television programmes aimed to make foods, ingredients and equipment accessible to everyone. She hopes to reintroduce people to the basics of ingredients and their preparation and pass on the pleasures of cooking and producing perfect food each time.

Jamie Oliver

Jamie Oliver represents a younger generation of chefs. His cooking is fun to watch but this does not mean he does not know what he is talking about. His experience at catering college and working with top chefs means he has a vast knowledge of food. Jamie wants to share his knowledge and to enable other people to enjoy preparing and cooking food as he does. He appeals to all age groups as he prepares a particular style of food that is simple, delicious and home cooked. He believes in stripping down restaurant methods to the reality of home cooking – making it simple so that cooking and eating is an experience to be shared with family and friends.

Think about it!

ABC FPT Investigate one of these chefs. You could perhaps try out one of their recipes or find out about food from another country.

Plenary

From this information it can be seen that some cooks and chefs have influenced the types and styles of food that we eat.

Celebrity chefs 2

Objectives

In this lesson you will:

- analyse a range of products developed by a celebrity chef
- understand how food is fashion and how equipment is designed.

It's interesting to see just how many cookery books have been written by television or celebrity chefs. These chefs have a great influence on the cooking and eating habits of the general public. Are they more influential than those people who write books but don't appear on television? Perhaps you think the most influential cooks or chefs are those who have a range of ready-prepared meals and desserts named after them. One cook who has published books and had a range of food products named after her, but who never appeared on television is Linda McCartney. She was famous for giving vegetarian cookery and vegetarian meals a high profile in shops and supermarkets.

Linda McCartney

Linda McCartney began to write books as a way of handing down recipes to her family and as a way of encouraging others to cook without using meat. Her recipes found their way into supermarkets in the form of ready meals, vegetarian sausages and many other products. So how do you think the different recipes were selected to devise a range of vegetarian products?

The main idea behind the Linda McCartney range of products was that all the products were vegetarian – they would not include meat or fish, but they could include dairy products such as eggs, cheese and milk. As meat and fish supply us with protein, these were replaced by alternatives: pulses, textured vegetable protein (TVP) and Quorn™.

The Linda McCartney range includes the following frozen products:

- shepherds pie
- flame-grilled burgers

A   *A product from the Linda McCartney range*

- lasagne
- vegetable stew and dumplings
- sausage rolls
- deep country pies
- sausages.

Think about it!

1   **D** If you had to add one or two new products to Linda McCartney's range, how would you go about it?

2   **ICT** Carry out some research into the products available in Linda McCartney's range. You may not be able to access the whole range but one or two products would be enough.

a) Find out and record your findings about the main ingredients, any ingredients that supply protein and the typical amounts portion size. You could use a table similar to the one in **E**.

Name of product	Protein supplied by:	Package size:	Main ingredient	Seasonings
Product 1				
Product 2				

E

b) Add any other categories that you think are relevant to the research.

3. Include some taste testing to find out what consumers think about the products. Decide whether it is better to use a product attribute or profile test, or a rating test. Which would give the results needed to make decisions about extending the range of products available?

4. **ABC** Would a short questionnaire help to gather information? Questions could ask what types of product consumers would like to see in the range or how they would like products to be modified to suit their tastes. The results could be displayed as charts.

📺 Extending a range

Once you have completed the research, decisions can be made about how to extend this particular range of products.

Designer equipment

Now let us take some time to consider 'designer' equipment for the kitchen. Does this equipment encourage people to prepare and cook food, is it more efficient or effective than standard equipment, or do people just buy it because it looks good in their kitchen? Photos **B**, **C** and **D** show different fruit squeezers or juicers, designed over a number of years. All of these show how the design of equipment has changed over the years and particularly to meet consumer demand for designer items. Perhaps another reason for the change in design is that the modern versions are more efficient?

B A traditional glass lemon squeezer

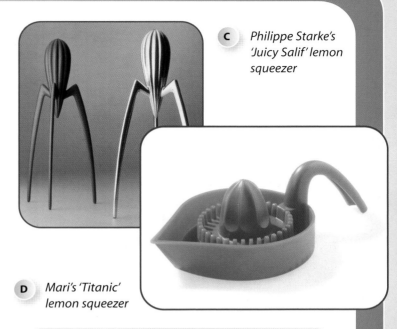

C Philippe Starke's 'Juicy Salif' lemon squeezer

D Mari's 'Titanic' lemon squeezer

Think about it!

Carry out some research into other equipment that may be found in the kitchen, such as graters, kettles, kitchen knives, saucepans, salt and pepper cellars. Comment on the different styles of equipment and include your views on aspects such as colour, size, price, target market, and why are they that particular size and shape. If you have the opportunity, you could evaluate the items to find out which are the most effective and efficient when in use.

Perhaps you have some ideas or developments of your own which you could sketch and annotate?

Sources for research

Some websites which you could use for research can be accessed via www.heinemann.co.uk/hotlinks. Enter the code 2183P.

Books:
The Dream Factory (2001) by Alberto Alessi
Alessi (1999) by Michael Collins
The Product Book (2000) by Catherine McDermott

Plenary

From these pages you will have learned how different types of research can help extend your ideas and give you more information about a particular product or range of products. You will also understand how trying out different equipment can broaden your knowledge of design and effectiveness.

Selecting materials

Objectives

In this lesson you will:

- evaluate products
- design products to meet different needs
- consider the influences of food from different cultures on products available in shops and supermarkets.

Key words

diversity   variety

Spoilt for choice!

People demand a choice of food wherever they are eating, whether it is in a restaurant, at a motorway service station or in a shopping mall. Each outlet has to make sure they are able to offer a choice of food products to suit people's demands. There are many reasons for this **diversity**.

- Personal choice: some people decide to follow a vegetarian diet, eating no fish or meat.
- Special dietary needs: some people with certain illnesses such as heart disease may have to follow a low-fat diet.
- Religious dietary rules: some foods are forbidden for Muslims, Jews, Hindus or Buddhists.
- Cultural differences: in some parts of Europe horsemeat is considered to be a delicacy, and in parts of Sierra Leone rats are grilled whole and then eaten!

There is a huge range of foods and ready-prepared meals available for different people with different needs and for people who just want to try something a little bit out of the ordinary.

Evaluating a ready-prepared meal

Look at the ready-prepared meal (**A**) and at the possible questions consumers might ask themselves before they decide to buy it (**B**).

A

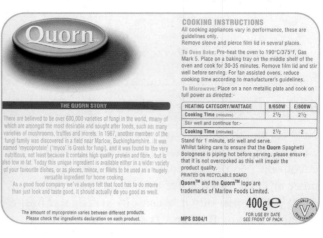

Consumer questions	Manufacturer's criteria
Is this for a vegetarian? Is this for a vegan?	Product should be suitable for a vegan or vegetarian
How many people is it for? Is it a main meal for one?	To serve one as a main meal (approx. 300g)
Can it be reheated in a microwave or an oven?	Must be able to be reheated in either an oven or a microwave
Can I freeze it for later?	Must be suitable for home freezing
Do I have to serve anything else with it, such as vegetables?	Serving suggestion – it's a complete meal, nothing else needed
Has it got green peppers in it, as I don't like them?	Do not include green peppers in recipe
It must contain less than 10g fat per 100g – does it?	Check nutritional values: less than 10g fat per 100g

B   *Questions about a ready-prepared meal*

Most of these answers can be found by looking at the information on the packaging and the labelling. The questions can be rephrased in the form of criteria or a set of needs that the manufacturer uses to help design this or other similar products. Look at table **B** again. These criteria could be used to evaluate the product. We are able to see if the product, in this case the Quorn™ pasta dish, did meet the needs for which it was designed and manufactured. The criteria could also be used to suggest improvements.

Evaluation checklist

- The product should be suitable for a vegetarian, containing no meat or fish. (✓)
- It should have been enough for 1 portion, >300g. (✓)
- It can be reheated in a microwave or an oven. (✓)
- It is suitable for home freezing. (✓)
- It contains no green peppers. (✓)
- Nutritional value, <10g fat per 100g. (✓)

This evaluation shows that this product was suitable for the intended purpose.

Foods of other cultures

There are hundreds of new products developed every year. Foods from particular countries around the world have always been popular, but now more products come from specific regions with their own particular flavours and ingredients. Research carried out by supermarkets and chefs means that more regional dishes are available to the consumer. The range of meals in **C** shows the diversity of ready-prepared dishes available.

FPT Seasonings

D Try out some seasonings to make a spicy rice or vegetable dish. You may want to make the dish to illustrate seasonings of a particular country or just experiment with different seasonings. There are individual seasonings and flavourings which could be used or you could try using a ready-made component of spices.

C

Think about it!

1 **ABC** Take a look at the food products in **C** and then write down a set of needs (or criteria) which each product may be designed to meet. Identify who you think might choose them and for what reasons.

2 **ABC** Write out a description of the differing characteristics of the products in **C**. You may want to comment on flavourings, seasonings and ingredients.

3 **TS** How, do you think, have the designers of these ready-prepared meals made sure they are authentic to the particular region?

4 **TS** Think about the flavouring ingredients of the products. Make a list of all those which have been used. Then either carry out research or sensory evaluation to find out what they are and what flavour they give the product.

5 **TS ICT** Think about region, either locally or from the wider world, and carry out research to find out the typical and traditional foods and their seasonings. Record your findings as a mood board (see page 45) using photographs and any other relevant information.

Plenary

You should be aware of the needs of different people and how to evaluate products. You should be able to identify some of the needs which products are designed to meet and you should have a greater understanding of the influences which different countries have had on food available in shops and supermarkets.

Adapting products

Objectives

In this lesson you will learn to adapt products to meet different dietary needs.

Key words

characteristics

In order to make sure that everyone is satisfied with what is on offer at a restaurant, on an aeroplane or at a leisure park, there has to be choice. It is easy to make products for the majority of consumers who do not have a special diet or do not mind eating meat, but what about those who do?

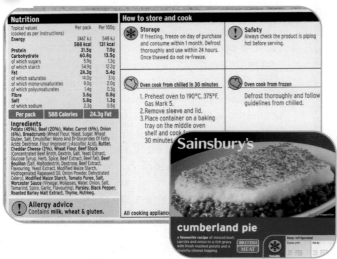

A classic British dish

A shows the ingredients label and packaging for a Cumberland pie, which is described as a 'classic' British dish. We will consider all the different ways the pie could be modified or adapted to make it suitable for a whole range of people with different dietary needs while still keeping the same characteristics. But first let us identify the different characteristics (parts) of Cumberland pie.

- At the bottom there is minced beef, carrots and onion in small pieces with a rich gravy.
- On top there is mashed potato, with a topping of grated cheese and breadcrumbs to make it crunchy.

topping of grated cheese and breadcrumbs

mashed potato

minced beef with carrots, onion and gravy

A vegetarian dish

If a vegetarian wanted to buy this food product, what would have to be changed to make sure it was similar to the original idea and contained similar nutritional values, but was suitable for them?

Vegetarians still need the same nutrients as everybody else but they do not want to eat fish or meat. As these two foods provide us with the majority of our protein requirements (for growth and repair, and a little for energy) it is important to replace them with other foods that provide protein. The best replacement proteins are cheese, milk, eggs, peas, beans, lentils, Quorn™, TVP or soya bean curd. So to make the pie suitable for a vegetarian we could change the minced beef for Quorn™ or a mixture of pulses (chick peas and red kidney beans for example) and use a vegetable-based stock rather than a beef stock. Use a dietary analysis program to check if the changes would provide similar nutrients. Changing the meat and the stock would have a similar outcome but also make the product suitable for a vegetarian.

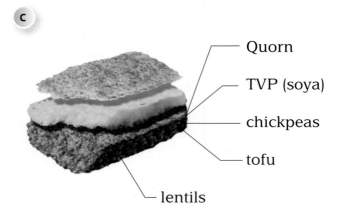

Quorn

TVP (soya)

chickpeas

tofu

lentils

A low-fat dish

Many people are advised to cut down on fats and eat a low-fat diet. We know from the balanced plate idea that fatty foods should only be eaten in small amounts. Recommendations for average adults are that men eat no more than 95g and women no more than 70g of fat per day. Many processed foods contain a high percentage of fat to make them taste better so how could we cut down on fat in this product? There are a number of options such as to use very lean minced beef, which contains less fat, or to use low-fat cheese on the topping.

A gluten-free dish

Another option could be to make the product gluten free. Gluten is the protein found particularly in wheat flour to which some people are allergic. On the ingredients label there are a number of components containing flour. What would happen if they were taken out? The pie would probably taste similar without the breadcrumbs, but flour is also used as a thickener for the gravy. What could you suggest as a alternative thickener instead of wheatflour? Can you suggest more than one alternative? All the Indian dishes mentioned earlier are gluten free. Check back to see if they included a thickener. If not, how were they thickened?

Adding fruit and vegetables

One of the recommendations for a healthy diet is to eat more fruit and vegetables. How would you add more fruit or vegetables to the Cumberland pie? One suggestion is to serve the pie with a side vegetable. You could also add more vegetables to the bottom layer – more carrot and perhaps sweetcorn, mushrooms or peas as well. Tomatoes could be added to the bottom layer either as puree or chopped up, or to the top of the pie as a garnish or decoration. All these changes will make the Cumberland pie different but it will still have similar characteristics.

The Cumberland pie can change in other ways to make it suitable for other groups of consumers. Some people have other dietary rules concerned with their beliefs. Different religions have dietary rules about the foods that are eaten or the way they are prepared and cooked. Your teacher will give you information about different religions and then you can make decide whether or not the Cumberland pie is an appropriate product for someone with any of these beliefs.

Think about it!

D We have looked at a number of changes that could be made to the standard recipe of the Cumberland pie. Does this mean that the company who initially produced the Cumberland pie could manufacture a whole range of ready-prepared meals based around the original idea? Imagine that you are the development manager for the company who produces Cumberland pies. From the ideas and suggestions made so far, make a list of the ways you could alter the product. Here are some suggestions to think about:

- different dietary, cultural and religious variations
- using seasonal ingredients
- using unusual combinations of ingredients
- using ingredients that correspond to a festival or local tradition (that is where the pie came from in the first place).

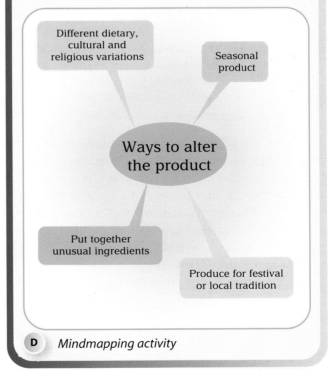

D *Mindmapping activity*

Plenary

This information should have helped you recognize that there are people who have different dietary needs and how these can be reconciled.

Combining components

Objectives

In this lesson you will:

- understand how and why different components are combined when making shortcrust pastry
- consider the functions of components in shortcrust pastry
- make shortcust pastry
- develop some alternatives.

It is important to understand that when ingredients are combined in different ways the outcomes may be very different. Many foods can be eaten just as they are, and this is fine for things such as apples, milk, or carrots. However if we only ate individual foods like this our daily diet might become very boring!

Think about it!

Make a list of all the foods that you can eat just as they are. Does your list have more than twenty foods on it? Explain whether or not you could eat just these foods for a whole week? Explain your answer.

Foods are mixed together in many different ways to give a larger variety of products. What you would think if you were given a plate with a pile of sugar, flour and butter on it instead of a tasty shortbread biscuit, or a plate with minced beef, an egg and a chopped onion instead of a beefburger (**A**)? With this in mind, let us look at combining ingredients in a bit more detail. It is simple to mix some ingredients together, such as flour with sugar or milk with eggs, as these have similar consistencies. However, you may come across problems when you try to mix ingredients with different consistencies together like flour with margarine, sugar with butter, or oil with vinegar.

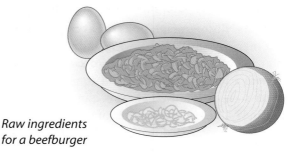

A *Raw ingredients for a beefburger*

Shortcrust pastry

There are several different ways of combining ingredients. The one we are going to focus on is the rubbing in method that combines fat and flour to make shortcrust pastry. Shortcrust pastry is a popular type of pastry used for both savoury and sweet food products such as quiche, pasties, jam tarts and fruit pies. Many ready-prepared meals also contain shortcrust pastry. To combine the fat with the flour it is rubbed in by hand – only half the amount of fat to the amount of flour should be used otherwise the mixture gets too sticky.

Each of the components in shortcrust pastry has a different function:

- the flour is for bulking
- the fat is to make the pastry 'short' (crumbly)
- the water is to bind (stick) the flour and fat together when they have been combined.

Each component must be included to make sure the pastry looks and tastes good. However, the components may be varied in order to develop different outcomes in taste, texture and appearance. The spider diagram in **B** shows how these ideas can be developed.

🔲 Shortcrust pastry

D A recipe for shortcrust pastry could be used to make a sweet or savoury pie. You will practise both the rubbing in method and rolling out the pastry.

You may be able to try out some of these different types of shortcrust pastry to make samples of your alternative ideas.

 **Potato pastry**

Try mixing half the amount of flour with an equal amount of mashed potato. Evaluate the result. Remember to think about texture, taste and appearance.

B

plain white

self-raising white

Flour

wholemeal (extra fibre, different colour and texture)

mix of wholemeal and white

lard (short pastry but no colour)

mix of lard and margarine

Shortcrust pastry

Fat

block margarine

butter (flavour and colour)

cold water

egg

Liquid

milk

tomato juice (flavour and different colour)

Testing your product

How do you know whether the new pastry will be liked by consumers? Try some sensory evaluation, this time with consumer testing using a hedonic ranking test. This tests how much a product is liked from 'extreme like' to 'extreme dislike'. Present the testers with two or more different pastry samples and ask them to mark on the five-point scale the point they think represents their view of the product. You could also record their comments (see **D**).

You could try using a difference test to see if there is any difference between two or more samples. Food manufacturers use these sensory analysis tests in product development, for example, to see if a low-fat version of a product can be picked out from a regular version, or if a new flavouring can be identified in a product.

Sample number:		Tick	Comments
1	Like a lot		
2	Like a little		
3	Neither like nor dislike		
4	Dislike a little		
5	Dislike a lot		

C *Hedonic ranking test for pastry*

Think about it!

1   What should 'good' shortcrust pastry look and taste like? Make a list of sensory descriptors to explain the taste, texture and appearance.

2   Look at diagram **C**.

a) **ABC** Develop and add some more of your own ideas as alternatives.

b) Compile a table to list the ingredients, functions, sensory properties and nutritional properties of the alternative shortcrust pastry.

c) **ICT** Use a nutritional analysis program to check how the changes make a difference to the nutritional content of the alternative pastry. Consider whether this will affect your choice of ingredients or not.

Plenary

You should have learned how to make shortcrust pastry and how to adapt it into different varieties. You should have used hedonic ranking to see how consumers liked your ideas.

Changing the recipe

Objectives

In this lesson you will:

- learn that cooking foods gives more variety
- investigate how to go about choosing appropriate ingredients for products

Many foods can be eaten uncooked, but cooking (heating) gives us many more alternatives. To illustrate this, think about the number of ways in which potatoes can be prepared, cooked and eaten.

Meat

Meat is one ingredient that needs cooking to make it safe to eat, easier to digest and more appetising. Meat is a valuable source of high-quality protein and is a good source of vitamin B and iron. Look in any butcher's window and you will see all kinds and cuts of meat for sale. But how do you or a food manufacturer know which one to choose?

The following are some questions to ask when choosing meat.

- Do I need a thin cut of meat (chops or steak that can be grilled or fried)?
- Do I want a thick cut or joint which needs a longer, slower method of cooking?
- What colour should it be?
- Could I use a different meat?
- How can I make sure the meat is tender and easy to digest?
- How much fat should there be?

A *Which sort of meat should you choose?*

- Do I want a bone in the meat?
- Which method of cooking should I use for the meat I choose?

Minced meat

One popular type of meat used in meals today is minced beef, pork or lamb. Minced meat is included in many ready-prepared meals such as Cumberland pie, moussaka and many more. Minced meat may be used because it is quick to cook and little or no preparation is needed if it is bought straight from a butcher's shop. But which minced meat should a manufacturer choose and how can they make sure it is the same each time? Look at the two samples of minced beef in **B**. One contains much more fat than the other and is cheaper. But even though the lean mince might be twice the price, it may still taste the same.

B

If you were a food manufacturer how would you decide which sample to use for the food product you were going to make in large quantities? Many manufacturers use a test kitchen which could:

- prepare and cook the same product with the different qualities of minced beef and compare the outcome, tasting and asking people to comment
- check the visible fat before the meat was minced
- dry fry both samples to see how much fat came out of each
- carry out some nutritional analysis to see the proportion of fat each sample contains.

When the quality and amount of minced beef has been decided upon, this must be repeated every time so the specification for the minced beef may say '100kg raw minced beef with 30% of visible fat ± 10 %'. Can you explain exactly what this means?

The same questions must be asked before choosing any ingredient for a food product – which ingredient should be used? The choice of ingredient may depend on the amount of profit the manufacturer wants to make rather than the health of its customers, or it may depend on who the meal is being developed for.

Value added

The shelves of supermarkets and shops also contain products, including meat, which are classed as 'value-added'. In the case of meat it means that the consumer is not just buying a pork chop or a chicken but a product which has been processed to give the consumer more choice and to make preparation even easier. Ready-prepared meals come into this category as do products such as ready-prepared kebabs or barbecue meats with a particular seasoning or flavouring.

Think about it!

ABC **ICT** Read the information on organic meat production, GM food production, meat analogues and British Farm Standards carefully and then choose one aspect on which to carry out further research. You could use books, leaflets the Internet and newspapers to find information. Try to find out about the issues and the possible benefits, resources, costs and other consequences to us, the consumers. Record all the information ready to share it with the rest of your class.

Organic meat

Farmers are required to ensure the following.

- All aspects of animal welfare are tightly controlled, including rearing, shelter, feeding and transportation.
- Only natural foods are fed to animals with the emphasis on home-grown organic forage.
- Growth promoters are not permitted.
- Stock levels are lower, so animals have more room and proper access to the outdoors.

- Animal medicines may be used under the guidance of a vet and only as a last resort. They may not be routinely used in feed.
- Transport and slaughtering are carefully monitored to minimize stress.

Genetically modified food production

Genetically modified foods can be produced to provide a food with a higher nutritional value, for example, to add more protein to rice. Animals may be reared to be more resistant to disease and may grow faster with the use of growth hormones. Plant crops may have a longer shelf life and the use of chemical fertilizers and pesticides may increase production.

Meat analogues (see pages 58–9)

These are foods that can be used in the same way as meat but have a different structure. They include soya bean products such as textured vegetable protein (TVP) or tofu and myco-protein products.

British Farm Standard

This logo assures consumers that the product has been produced on a British farm to British Standards. What does this mean?

The Soil Association

This logo is a certification mark found on over 70 per cent of the UK's organic food. It guarantees that the food or drink has been produced to rigorous organic standards.

DMA Design a ready meal

D Produce a prototype of a suitable ready-prepared meal for a person with special dietary needs. You have looked at some of the decisions which have to be made about each component before you can develop a product or write a specification for the product.

Plenary

You have learnt about many of the different criteria and issues to consider when choosing ingredients for new food products.

Packaging and labelling

Most of this unit of work has been about ready-prepared meals and you have seen that there are a wide variety of packaging materials used to protect these meals. But what happens to the packaging afterwards? Packaging has a number of important functions including:

- to protect food products from damage during transport and storage
- to protect them from deterioration – they may be part of the preservation process, for example tin cans
- to describe and identify the contents
- to help stop tampering and contamination
- to advertise the product.

Table **B** explains the reasons why some of the packing materials have been used.

Product	Type of material	Advantages	Disadvantages
Cola can	Aluminium	Lightweight, **recyclable**, impermeable	Not **biodegradable**
Take-away burger container	Polystyrene	Keeps in heat	Not environmentally friendly

 B   *Advantages and disadvantages of different packaging materials*

Environmentally-friendly packaging

There are some packages which are biodegradable, environmentally-friendly packages. Some are made from a totally natural ingredient – potato. Wherever possible, the potato is the waste produce from potato chip processing plants.

Recycling

Excessive packaging is another issue. In some parts of Europe each household has to pay for every bin of rubbish which is collected each week. Initially this led to shoppers disposing of excessive packaging at the supermarkets where they had been shopping. The supermarkets then had to pay for disposal of the rubbish so quite quickly changes were made for manufacturers to use less packaging. Consider the

Tin   Glass jar with tamper proof lid

Polystyrene burger container

Plastic pot   Plastic wrapper   Box or cereal box

A   *There are many types of materials that can be used to package foods*

C

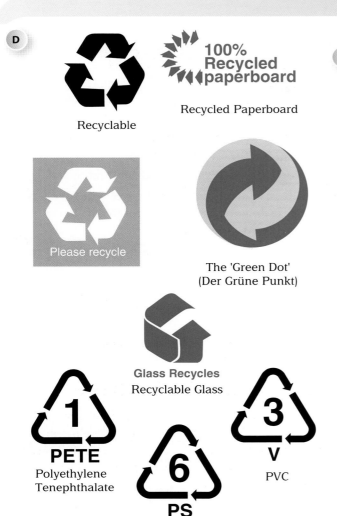

Recyclable

Recycled Paperboard

Please recycle

The 'Green Dot'
(Der Grüne Punkt)

Glass Recycles
Recyclable Glass

PETE
Polyethylene
Tenephthalate

PS
Polystyrene

V
PVC

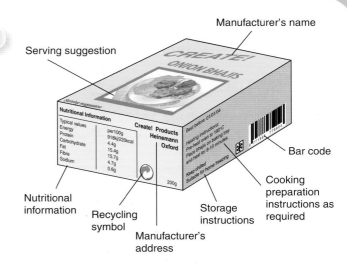

Serving suggestion

Manufacturer's name

Nutritional
information

Recycling
symbol

Manufacturer's
address

Storage
instructions

Cooking
preparation
instructions as
required

Bar code

two packets of biscuits in **C**. Which one would you describe as more environmentally friendly?

D shows all the recyclable symbols you could find on packaging. How many of these can you find on all your food packaging at home? Find out what your local council are doing about recycling rubbish.

Information on packaging

Recycling symbols are just one piece of information that is found on packaging. Some pieces of information must be there by law, including the name of the food, the name and address of the manufacturer or seller, storage instructions, any cooking or preparation instructions, weight or volume, a list of ingredients and any special claims (**E**). Some manufacturers add other information to help the consumer. The label might show the recycling symbols already mentioned, smart codes, serving suggestions, price and nutritional information.

Think about it!

1 Extend Table **B** to explain why other products have different packaging materials. Give advantages and disadvantages of each.

2 **ICT** **ABC** Find out more about environmentally friendly packaging. Go to this website and click on this activity to get started: www.heinemann.co.uk/hotlinks. Work with another person to discuss the possible benefits of using this type of biodegradable packaging as opposed to the traditional foil or paper tray. Write a report together about your views.

3 **ABC** Is there any motivation for buying 'loose' products such as mushrooms in a paper bag rather than in a plastic carton with plastic film covering? Explain your answer.

4 **ABC** The ready-prepared meals include the name of the product but also had a description of the meal, such as, 'diced fresh aubergine in a tasty medium-spiced tomato sauce with onion and fresh coriander' or 'delicious Quorn mushroom protein pieces with torchio pasta in a rich and creamy red pesto sauce'.

Write a description for one of the meals you have made, using descriptive adjectives to persuade consumers to buy your product and describe your product in more detail.

Plenary

You should be more aware of the need to minimize environmental damage when selecting materials for packaging food products and should have an understanding of information you can find on a label.

Nutritional labelling

Objectives

In this lesson you will use and build on nutritional knowledge to learn to interpret and use nutritional labelling.

Some consumers think the most important piece of information on a label is the nutritional information so they can see that they are buying a 'healthy' product. To use this information you need some knowledge about nutrition. If you look at the information in **A** you will be able to 'read and use' a nutritional label. Some of the information you already know.

Protein

Protein is needed for growth and repair. In our developed country we all get enough protein so this information is unimportant except if you are buying a vegetarian product and you want to check that it is providing as much protein as a similar meat product.

Fat

Fat is used for energy. It is very easy to eat more fat than you need. We should be eating no more than 75g–95g of fat each day. 20g of fat per 100g of food is high. 3g of fat per 100g of food is low. Most labels now break down fats into three types because some fats are better for you than others.

Nutrition Information		
TYPICAL VALUES	Per Onion Bhaji	Per 100g As Sold
ENERGY	428kJ/103kcal	918kJ/220kcal
PROTEIN	2.1g	4.4g
CARBOHYDRATE	7.2g	15.4g
of which sugars	2.1g	4.6g
FAT	7.3g	15.7g
of which saturates	0.7g	1.5g
FIBRE	2.2g	4.7g
SODIUM	0.3g	0.6g

- Saturated fats are animal fats like lard and butter. They help develop cholesterol in blood vessels that can cause heart attacks.
- Mono-unsaturated fat is found in olive oil. Some people think this is the healthiest fat to eat.
- Polyunsaturated fats are all other vegetable fats. These do not cause cholesterol to develop and are considered 'healthier' fats.
- Essential fatty acids (omega-3 and omega-6) are very important for our health. They are found in oily fish and grains. Some packaging will advertise the presence of these in the food.

Carbohydrate

Carbohydrate is used for energy. It is considered better to eat carbohydrate for energy than fat. But there are 'good' and 'bad' carbohydrates. Sugar is a 'bad' carbohydrate as it does not provide any other nutrients and once digested it releases energy very quickly. 10g of sugar in 100g of food is high and 2g of sugar in 100g of food is low.

Starch is a 'good' carbohydrate. Healthy-eating guidelines suggest we should be eating more starchy foods. Starchy foods provide other nutrients, for example, flour provides starch, vitamin B and calcium. So, it is important to check what kind of carbohydrate your food product contains.

Fibre

Fibre (NSP) is needed to keep the digestive system working properly. It prevents constipation and is believed to prevent some cancers. We should be eating 18 grams of a fibre a day. Many people don't eat enough fibre. 3g of fibre in 100g of food is high and 0.5g of fibre is low. Remember, you want large amounts of fibre and small amounts of fat!

Sodium/salt

Sodium/salt adds flavour to foods and helps preserve foods. Salt is another nutrient that we can easily eat too much of. Too much salt can cause high blood pressure and strokes. We should have no more than 7g of salt a day. 0.5g of salt in 100g of food is high and 0.2g of salt is low.

Energy

Different people need different amounts of energy each day. The average is 2000 kcal for women and 2500 kcal for men. The amount you need depends on your age, size and how active you are in your job and leisure time. People who are trying to be careful about their weight often look for ready-prepared meals with less than 300kcals in them.

Vitamins and minerals

Some food manufacturers choose to include more detailed nutritional information and provide information about vitamins and minerals (see **B**). When information is provided about vitamins and minerals, it shows the percentage of the recommended daily amount (RDA) provided by the product. Often food manufacturers claim that their product is high in a certain vitamin or mineral so then show this on the nutritional label.

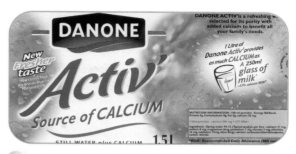

C   Calcium makes strong bones and teeth

Food manufacturers also like to claim that their foods are low in the 'bad' nutrients; some baked beans have reduced sugar and salt in them. Did you know that Heinz have gradually reduced the amount of salt and sugar in their tins of baked beans over several years?

Think about it!

1. 123 Find out how much sugar there is in a 100g portion of baked beans and 100g of tomato sauce?

2. Look at the two biscuit products in **D**.

    a) If you were to look only at the front of these packets, which one would you think is healthier? Explain your answer.

    b) Collect two biscuit packets and compare the nutritional value of them. Explain which is the healthiest and why.

    c) Some products claim to be 95% fat free. Find out what this means.

D

NUTRITION INFORMATION

TYPICAL COMPOSITION	A 40g serving with 125ml semi-skimmed milk provides	100g (3½ oz) provide
Energy	709kJ/168kcal*	1147kJ/271kca
Protein	9.3g	13.0g
Carbohydrate	23.7g	43.6g
of which sugars	13.5g	18.0g
Fat	4.0g*	5.0g
of which saturates	1.7g	0.8g
mono-unsaturates	0.9g	0.9g
polyunsaturates	1.4g	3.3g
Fibre**	11.6g	29.0g
Sodium	0.3g	0.7g
VITAMINS/MINERALS		
Vitamin D	1.7 µg (34% RDA)	4.3 µg (86% RDA)
Vitamin E	1.0 mg (10% RDA)	2.4 mg (24% RDA)
Thiamin	0.5 mg (38% RDA)	1.2 mg (86% RDA)
Riboflavin	0.8 mg (49% RDA)	1.4 mg (87% RDA)
Niacin	7.2 mg (40% RDA)	15.3 mg (85% RDA)
Vitamin B6	0.8 mg (38% RDA)	1.7 mg (85% RDA)
Folic Acid	87.5 µg (44% RDA)	200.0 µg (100% RDA)
Vitamin B12	0.9 µg (86% RDA)	0.9 µg (90% RDA)
Calcium	286.0 mg (36% RDA)	340.0 mg (43% RDA)
Iron	2.9 mg (20% RDA)	7.0 mg (50% RDA)
Magnesium	101.8 mg (34% RDA)	220.0 mg (73% RDA)
Zinc	3.3 mg (22% RDA)	7.0 mg (47% RDA)
RDA = Recommended Daily Allowance		

B   Nutritional information from a cereal packet.

Plenary

Now you should be able to use the nutritional information on a package to make an informed choice when buying food products.

Running a mini-enterprise

Objectives

In this lesson you will learn how to set up a mini-enterprise.

If you were at a school spring fair and saw the two stalls (**A** and **B**) full of food products for sale, which stall would you buy from? Listen to the story of Class 1's experience and answer the questions.

A

B

Class 1's brief

Class 1's brief was to design and make a simple product to sell at a fair. The product must be suitable for batch production. You should now follow the same brief. Your design and any decoration need to be simple so that it is easy to manufacture.

To be successful with this design brief you must:

- remember the mistakes Class 1 made
- design a product that will sell
- develop and make prototypes to see if they are liked and are easy to make (manufacture)
- produce the product efficiently and to the same high quality
- market (advertise) the product successfully
- cover costs and make a profit
- work as a team.

Working as a team

Why is it important to work as team? Perhaps if we look at a real food manufacturing company we can find out about teamwork. Let us look at Farmhouse Biscuits, the company we visited in Unit 5. This company employs 150 people. They all have different jobs and are successful because while they concentrate on their particular jobs they also work as a team.

C *John Sutton, quality manager, part of the production team – he looks after safety and hygiene*

D *Philip McIvor, the managing director – he runs the company*

E *Mike Cruise, the buyer for raw materials, also part of the production team – he controls the delivery and quality of ingredients*

F Stuart West, works manager – he makes sure the machinery is working

G Tony Birbeck, marketing manager – one of his main jobs is to design the tins some of the biscuits are packaged in

H Paula O'Sullivan, personnel manager – she employs new workers and then looks after them

All these people are employed for their particular talents. They work hard at their own job but also listen to other people to make sure the quality of the product is maintained.

Your own team

Your team needs to take on the various jobs required to run a business. What would be the best job for each member of your team? Think about each other's skills and abilities, but remember you will have to be flexible as some jobs will involve more work than others.

- The **project manager** will be the boss who will make sure everyone is carrying out their job well and on time but will also work hard producing the product when needed.

- The **production manager** will organize and plan how the product is made. He or she will decide how many people are needed for each unit operation and will also make sure that the quality of the product stays the same.

- The **finance manager** will look after the money. He or she will work out the unit cost of the product and then decide on a price to make a profit. The finance manager will hand out money for ingredients and collect the money when the

product is sold. He or she might find out different ways to get money to start the company for example issue shares.

- The **marketing manager** will think of different ways to advertise the product, such as designing posters and so on. He or she might design the packaging of the product.

- The **personnel manager** will help the production manager decide who in the team does different jobs. They both need to make sure everyone is happy in their work.

Once you have decided on your different jobs you need to decide on:

- the product you are going to make
- how it will be made
- how it will be marketed.

Some of these decisions need to be made by the whole team but some by one or two members. Detailed planning is needed. You need to complete some research to make sure your product will sell either before you decide on a product or when you are producing prototypes. Make sure the team is concentrating on all the points needed to be successful.

Think about it!

1. The food products on Class 1's stall don't look as attractive as the ones on Class 2's stall. Why not?

2. How could Class 1 have been more successful?

3. **ABC** Read through the story again and explain what Class 1 did wrong at each stage (in each lesson). Perhaps the first thing that was wrong was that there was no help or guidance from their form teacher.

Plenary

If you use the information on this page, plan well, co-operate with each other and work hard, your mini-enterprise will be a success.

Understanding food processes

Low-risk foods

If you want to make sure the food you sell is safe to eat, you need to include only low-risk foods. Low-risk foods are foods that do not provide ideal conditions for bacterial growth. Look back to pages 18 and 19 to remind yourself of the ideal conditions for bacterial growth.

Low-risk foods include:

- sugar-based confectionery such as sweets and icing
- high-sugar content foods such as jams, curds and marmalades
- high-acid content foods such as pickles and chutneys
- oils.

Look at the products included on the stall in **A** for some ideas of low-risk food products.

Methods of preserving food

Foods can be preserved by adding chemicals such as vinegar (an acid) and sugar to them. These are traditional methods of preservation that have been used for many years.

Vinegar

Vinegar is acetic acid. It has a pH of 3.5. Bacteria cannot survive in solutions below pH 4.5 so foods kept in vinegar solutions such as onions and cabbage last a long time and are low-risk foods. Pickles include vinegar as a main ingredient so these are low-risk foods too. Look at the list of ingredients on worksheet 9.3 for two pickle recipes. You will see that vinegar is an important ingredient.

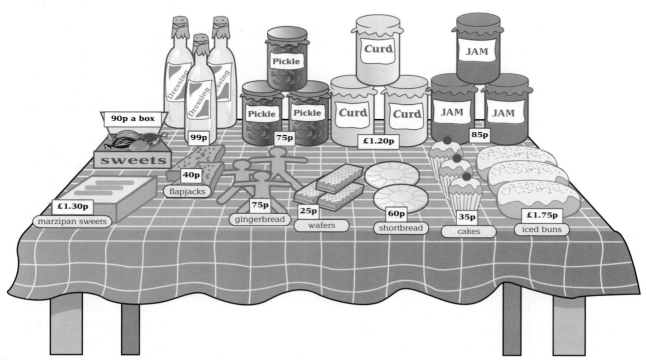

A   *This stall includes examples of low-risk food products. Can you identify which these are?*

Sugar

Sugar prevents bacteria from growing if it is used in a high concentration. The sugar content has to be 60 per cent of the final product. Bacteria just cannot survive in these heavy syrups. Sugar solutions act as a preservative in jams, curds and marmalade. Sugar is also used as a preservative in the bottling and freezing of fruit.

Sugar solutions are used in sweet making. The solution can be boiled to different temperatures to produce different characteristics that are used in a variety of sweets. Sugar boiled to 115°C makes fudge. If it is boiled to 138°C it makes toffee and to 145°C butterscotch. A sugar thermometer like the one in **B** is an essential piece of equipment when making sweets as it is very easy to overcook sugar solutions. Overheating will create a dark brown solution which tastes bitter.

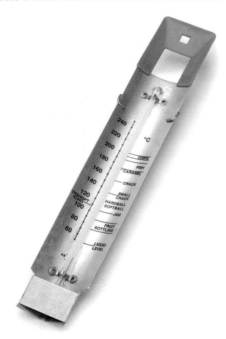

B   A sugar thermometer

Sugar is also a preservative when used in cakes and biscuits. Sugar helps these products to stay moist which keeps them in good condition for longer. This means they have a longer shelf life. Sugar keeps products moist because moisture is attracted to sugar. If treacle or golden syrup or even honey is used in a recipe, these cakes keep moist even longer because the sugar in these syrups (fructose) absorbs a lot of moisture from the atmosphere. So cakes such as parkin, gingerbread and flapjack have a very long shelf life.

Preservation is not the only function of sugar in cakes and biscuits. Sugar is also used to:

- add sweetness
- add flavour (strengthens the natural flavour of fruits)
- add colour – the sugar and flour interact to brown at a high temperature
- alter texture – sugar attracts water so there is less water for the protein (gluten) in flour to absorb. This means the gluten does not become stretched and doughy as happens during bread making, so a soft crumbly texture is produced.
- make products light and risen. When sugar and fat are 'creamed' (beaten together), the air which is beaten into the mixture sticks to the sugar crystals. The fat surrounds the air bubbles and 'traps' them in the mixture. Caster sugar gives the best results because of the large number of fine crystals. In granulated sugar the crystals are too big and there are not enough of them. In icing sugar the crystals are too small to work in this way.

Produce for the fair

You will need to choose the products you make carefully. Do you have enough time to make them? Do you have the skill or the specialist equipment to make them?

Think about it!

1   Find other recipes that use vinegar to preserve food. Some recipes will use **seasonal** ingredients. Decide when in the year these recipes should be used.

2   Lemon curd is just one of many curd recipes; coconut curd is another. Can you find recipes for other curds?

3   Cooking sugar to high temperatures can be very dangerous. Are there any sweets you could make that do not require special sugar thermometers and boiling sugar?

Plenary

Now you have learned about some low-risk foods, you must make prototypes of one or more to see if these products are liked and easy to make.

Quality assurance

Objectives

In this lesson you will:

- ● find out why quality assurance and quality control must be used if you are to be profitable
- ● learn that consumers place different quality values on food products
- ● consider how CAD and CAM can ensure repetitive quality.

Key words

quality assurance ensuring that products are of good quality and are safe

One of the reasons Class 1 made so little profit was because their products were not all of the same quality. What is wrong with the quality of the food products in **A**?

Quality counts

If you are to be successful you must produce a product efficiently and to the same high quality. Quality assurance is used in food manufacturing to make sure a guaranteed quality of product is made.

Quality assurance is achieved in a product by following a manufacturing specification and using quality controls. This manufacturing specification is like the specifications you have learned to write, but includes far more detail. It is concerned with:

- ● the quality and size of ingredients, for example soft cake flour not 'value' flour, finely-grated lemon rind and so on.
- ● the exact recipe with weights and a detailed description, for example 200g unsalted butter
- ● how the product should be made, including types of cooking methods, temperatures and cooling times
- ● specific tolerances, for example thickness of cookies, viscosity (runniness) of lemon curd
- ● finishing techniques, for example decorating a cake with a whole cherry in the centre, brush with whole-egg glaze before baking
- ● details of packaging such as shape, size and materials used, for example glass jar with metal lid
- ● design and wording of label including information and instructions (storage and shelf life).

A shows an example of a manufacturing specification for coconut ice.

Manufacturing specification		
Product name: Coconut ice	**Portion size:** 7 x 100g portions	
Specific ingredients	**Tolerances**	**Specific dimensions, packaging, description**
450g white granulated sugar		100g ±10g coconut ice in each bag, pieces 2cm square ±1cm
150g desicated coconut	Fine pieces <1cm	Plastic bag secured with tag to keep airtight
150ml fresh semi-skimmed milk	Tin should be greased and	
3ml red food colouring	measure 20cm × 15cm	
	Boil until temperature of	
	116°C is reached	
Storage	**Cooking methods**	
Chilled (1 – 4°C) = fresh	Boil until 116°C	
semi-skimmed milk		
Frozen (–18°C)	**Reheating instructions**	
Ambient = white granulated	Not applicable	
sugar, desicated coconut, red		
food colouring	**Ready-made components**	
	none	
Storage instructions		
Store in an airtight bag or container		

Nutritional information: Coconut ice:		
	Typical values	
	per 100g	per serving 125g
Energy	1533kJ 366kcal	1916kJ 458kcal
Protein	1.78g	2.23g
Carbohydrate of which sugar	63.5g 65.3g	81.6g 81.6g
Fat of which saturates	12.7g 10.9g	15.9g 13.6g
Fibre (NSP)	2.74g	3.43g
Sodium	0.02g	0.02g
Iron	0.73g	0.91g
Calcium	29.8g	37.3g
Vitamin A	4.5ug	5.63ug

ⓕ CAD/CAM

After you have made a prototype and tested it to see if people will buy it, you need to write a manufacturing specification to make sure the quality of the product stays the same every time it is made. You will be able to use quality control checks before, during and after the manufacturing process to make sure you match the manufacturing specification. Look back at pages 46 and 47 to remind yourself what these quality control checks are. Using manufacturing aids and CAD/CAM help control the quality of your product too.

Is quality worth paying for?

Which of the pots of lemon curd in **B** would you buy? Why? If you knew that jar 1 cost 70p and jar 2 cost £1.25p, which one would you buy? Some consumers would choose to buy jar 1 while others would choose to buy jar 2 even though it is more expensive. Some consumers think the quality of the product is worth paying extra money for. Quality is not just about packaging a product to look good. The appearance, taste and texture of the food have to be worth the extra money. Jar 2 may have a higher fruit content than jar 1 as this gives a richer taste.

B   Jar 1   Jar 2

There are other reasons that people will pay more money for a product:

- if it is a natural product with no artificial additives
- if it is organic
- if it is 'hand-made' – consumers think these products will be natural with no additives and be made in a traditional, better way
- if it is personalised – made especially for you.

Personalised products

C shows how CAD and CAM can be used to create a personalized product. In some supermarkets and bakeries/cake shops you can provide a photograph that you want on top of a cake. This is scanned into a computer where extra graphics and words can be added. This image is then printed onto edible paper using edible inks. When this printed paper is put onto fondant icing it merges with the icing to create a high-quality product. This process is not just used for one-off celebration cakes. An image can be repeated again and again or used on individual biscuits or cakes.

Think about it!

1   ⓉⓈ Can you think of any food products other than jam that cost more because of their high fruit content?

2   A good investigation would be to compare a hand-made product with a high-volume (mass produced) product. Some examples you could use are chocolates, biscuits, cakes, jams and curds. Compare them for taste, price, ingredients, appearance, amount and packaging.

Plenary

You should now understand how to use a manufacturing specification to produce quality food products. You have found out that quality means different things to different consumers and that people are prepared to pay more for certain products. You have been reminded that CAD and CAM are used to help produce quality products.

Bread

Objectives

In this lesson you will:

- find out how bread is made
- learn about the function of each ingredient.

Key words

fermentation a biological process that occurs when gas and heat are produced by micro-organisms (bacteria or yeast) as they convert organic material into energy needed to multiply

Before you start designing or modifying any food product for yourself or other consumers, you need to understand how that product is made and the purpose (function) of all the ingredients.

Bread has an important part to play in our daily diet. It is a starchy food that also contains fibre, or NSP (non starch polysaccharide) and plenty of vitamins and minerals. So it is a good idea to develop new types of bread and bread products to make sure that consumer demand remains high.

The ingredients of bread

Flour is the bulking ingredient of bread. It forms the structure of the product. Strong flour is used in bread making because it has a higher gluten (protein) content than other flours. Check the protein content on the side of the bag – it should be between 10.5 and 14.0 per cent. Gluten stretches to hold the carbon dioxide (CO_2) bubbles produced by the yeast. It gives the bread a chewy, doughy texture rather than a crumbly texture like cakes. The wheat for strong flour is grown extensively in Canada.

Yeast causes the bread to rise. It is a biological raising agent and can multiply continually if it is given the right conditions. Raising agents produce gases to make food products rise. Because it is a living organism, yeast needs warmth, food, moisture and time to grow. Yeast also needs energy to multiply, which it gets by converting sugar (from the flour) into alcohol and carbon dioxide gas. This is known as **fermentation**. Fresh yeast, dried yeast or easy blend yeast can be used.

A

Liquid is used to bind the flour together and help form the structure of the bread. The liquid needs to be warm or tepid (37°C) for the yeast to work effectively. If the liquid is too hot it kills the yeast; too cold and it slows the fermentation process.

Salt is used in small quantities (two per cent ratio to flour) to add flavour to the bread. Salt also strengthens the gluten and controls the action of yeast.

Fat is added to improve the texture of the bread, and to stop the bread going stale quickly.

Think about it!

1   Apart from yeast, what other living creatures need warmth, food, moisture and time to grow?
2   If you taste breads, you will be able to understand how the different ingredients and ways of cooking have changed the organoleptic properties of bread.

FPT Bread

D   Now that you understand why each ingredient in bread is needed, you need to find out how it is made. The process of making bread is quite different from that of biscuits and cakes. The method on worksheet 10.1 is a simple way of making bread. You should be able to make this during a one-hour lesson. Once you know and understand bread making, you can add or substitute ingredients and methods.

Different breads

Bread is very versatile. Think about ordinary white bread and the many different ways it is sold: loaf, bloomer, burger roll, finger roll, thick-sliced, thin-sliced, crusty or soft. In what other ways can you buy white bread?

White bread is not the only type of bread you can buy. The quantities or types of the basic ingredients can be altered to produce all kinds of different breads. For example, if milk is used instead of water the texture of the bread becomes softer, and if wholemeal flour is used instead of white flour the bread becomes chewy and more solid.

Extra ingredients can be added too. Extra fat can be added to alter the flavour and texture of the bread, and other ingredients such as sugar or flour can be added. Bread can be cooked in different ways too. Steam can be pumped into an oven to make a crispy crust. Bread can be cooked at different temperatures, boiled, fried (doughnuts) or even steamed.

Look at the breads in **B** and find more examples of your own. Read how their different ingredients and production alter their tastes.

Croissant – lots of butter added for a rich, flaky bread.

Naan – a high temperature used during baking, extra ingredients such as meat, nuts or dried fruit can be added to the dough or stuffed inside.

Bagel – the dough is boiled then baked for a chewy texture.

Ciabatta – olive oil is added for flavour.

Stromboli – cheese and tomato is spread onto a flat dough and then rolled up; more cheese and herbs are sprinkled on top.

Brioche – egg, sugar and butter added to give it a rich cake-like texture and taste.

Chelsea bun – cinnamon and dried fruit spread onto flat dough, rolled and cut into buns, sugar crystals sprinkled on top.

Pretzel – rolled out into thin sticks, then twisted and baked for a crisp texture.

Think about it!

3   D   As you now know how to make bread, you can experiment with some of the ingredients. You could work in groups each changing or adding one ingredient. Then taste and evaluate your findings as a group. Completing experiments like this helps you to make decisions about ingredients to use when designing new products.

Plenary

You have learned about bread and the functions of extra ingredients as well as its basic ingredients.

B

Bread manufacturing

Objectives

In this lesson you will:

- find out how the making of most food products has changed over time, from one-off to high volume production

- learn about how computer-controlled systems are used to make these high volume foods.

A century and a half ago, housewives traditionally made their own bread and cooked it in the range. As times have changed and more and more women work out of the home, very few people today make their own bread every day. This change has been a gradual process as households have not only had less time to bake but also more money to spend on bought products. Nowadays, skilled bakers make better bread of a consistent quality.

Warburtons

In 1876 Ellen and Thomas Warburton ran a grocers shop in Bolton, Lancashire. One day Ellen decided to supplement their income by making extra bread to sell in the shop. That first day she made just four loaves and six flour cakes. They sold quickly so the next day she made double the amount and the day after double again. Ellen's bread became so popular that the Warburtons employed their nephew Henry to help them make and deliver the bread. The combination of Ellen's ingredients, an extra long cooking time and Henry's delivery around the town in a pony and cart proved very successful.

Eventually Henry bought the bakery business from his aunt and uncle. Later, his three sons took over from him. Today it is the fifth generation of the family who are running Warburtons bakery. As the bakery has expanded the company has moved to larger factories three times. They also export bread abroad. The bread production is now fully automated with computers controlling all the different processes. Millions of Warburtons loaves are produced each year. You can see some of the products made by Warburtons in photo **A**.

Warburtons use the Chorleywood bread process. Traditionally bread is left to rise for up to four hours. But when bread is made in large quantities there is not the time or space to use the traditional method. In 1961 the Chorleywood process was developed. Some of the proving time is reduced and replaced by a few minutes of intense mechanical mixing of the dough. Flour treatment agents (ascorbic acid – vitamin C) are added to the dough to make it rise more quickly. Other additives such as emulsifiers and preservatives are also added during the mass production of bread to extend its shelf life. This process is the most commonly used method for large-scale production.

Find out more about Warburtons by following this link: www.heinemann.co.uk/hotlinks.

Golden West Foods

Golden West Foods uses the Chorleywood method to make all the burger buns for McDonalds Restaurants.

Flour and other ingredients are delivered to the factory in tankers and stored in silos.

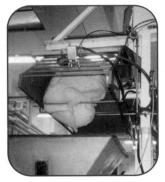

Most ingredients are piped into the mixer. Small quantities are added by hand. The dough is mixed and tipped out onto the start of the conveyor belt (**B**). A special machine divides the dough into bun sizes (**C**). The buns are left to rest for a half an hour (pre-proove). The buns go into trays. They go into the proving oven for 50 minutes. This oven is warm with 85 per cent humidity. The ordinary burger buns have water sprayed on them and sesame seeds sprinkled over them. This process is left out when big Mac and quarter pounder buns are made. It takes 25 minutes for the buns to pass through the oven. The oven is computer controlled. De-panning of the buns take place by suction. The buns are cooled on two spiral cooling towers (they go up one and down the other). A machine slices the buns in half. The buns are packed in twelves. They are stacked ready for transportation to the outlets.

FPT Bread

D Plan a batch or mass production of bread rolls in the classroom. Work out what equipment you have to help you, for instance: large mixers, electronic scales, conveyor oven, bread maker. Work out the unit operations and how many people are needed for each unit. Carry out this production.

Additives

Additives are added to much of the bread made in the UK today. They are added to food products during manufacturing to improve their flavour, colour, texture and keeping properties.

Think about it!

1 **D ABC** Draw a flow chart showing the input, process and output of the Golden West Foods system. Include the feedbacks that would take place during the system to make sure a quality product is produced. Most of these feedbacks will be computer-controlled but some will have to be carried out by people.

2 Compare how the McDonalds buns are made with how you have made bread in the Food Technology room. Write a flowchart of your bread making to help you with your comparison.

3 There are advantages and disadvantages of using additives.
   a) **ABC** Find out more about both natural and artificial emulsifiers and their function. You could use the Internet to help you.
   b) Today more consumers are demanding 'natural' food products. List the advantages and disadvantages of additives in this respect.

Plenary

You have learnt how the manufacture of food products changes over time, and how most of the bread in the UK is produced.

Craft bread

Objectives

In this lesson you will learn that some manufacturers consider other criteria, such as environmental issues and quality, more important than profit and volume.

Key words

organic products produced without the use of chemical pesticides, fungicides or herbicides, without the use of fertilisers or growth regulators or stimulants (that make crops or animals grow faster) and without using unnecessary antibiotics or intensive farming methods.

Not all the bread that we eat today is mass-produced in large factories. Some bread is still baked in 'craft' bakeries where the skill of the baker produces high quality bread. There is no legal definition of 'craft' bread in the UK. The term is sometimes used to describe bread that is made on a small scale, with some processes being completed manually. Often, however, the bread has been mass produced up to a certain stage, then frozen or chilled and transported to the outlet where it is finished by hand. 'Craft' baking should mean a continuous process of making bread using the skill of the baker to create inspirational recipes. In France, a boulangerie (bakery) cannot be called by this name unless it carries out the five stages of bread making in a continuous time frame.

The Village Bakery, Melmerby

The Village Bakery at Melmerby in Cumbria is an example of a real craft bakery. This is an **organic** bakery using traditional craftsmanship to make tasty and interesting breads and cakes baked in wood-fired ovens in a way which respects workers, customers and the environment. Only organic ingredients are used in the bakery. For three years in a row, the bakery has won the prestigious Soil Association Organic Food Award for its products.

Organic food production

Organic farmers follow a strict set of guidelines laid down by national and international law. They must keep thorough and accurate records of production processes and they must submit to annual and random inspections. These farmers will use traditional methods, such as crop rotation, to help keep soil free of pests and full of nutrients. They use natural composts and manure to fertilise the soil and rely on natural pest control by allowing insects to eat each other.

Organic food is becoming increasingly popular as consumers become more concerned about health, moral and ethical issues. Organic foods cost more because the farming methods need more time and labour. But, if more people buy them prices will fall.

B

United Kingdom approved organic certification bodies (as at 1st January 1995)	
Biodynamics Agricultural Association	
Irish Organic Farmers and Growers Association	
Organic Farmers and Growers	
Organic Food Federation	
Scottish Organic Producers Association	
Soil Association Organic Marketing Company	

Respect products

Respect is a new company that produces organic cakes which are available in supermarkets. Respect's philosophy is centred around:

- the honesty and integrity of the product
- caring about the environment we live in
- foods at their purest and finest
- supporting the Earth's ecosystems.

This philosophy is summed up by the message on their website which reads, 'Respect ... don't you deserve a little?'

C

D

Looking after the environment

The Village Bakery uses wood-fired ovens to bake their bread because wood is a renewable resource. It is one of the only bakeries that uses a high-output wood-fired oven. When the Village Bakery wanted to expand their production of bread they had to purchase a wood furnace. It has a capacity for 80 trays and is computer-controlled to produce the same quality bread and cakes every time. Special flues and filters reduce emissions to an absolute minimum and any extra heat is used in a greenhouse next door. The oven uses compacted brickets of sawdust.

Unlike coal, gas or oil, wood is renewable. If a 150-acre forest is harvested in rotation and replanted the wood would supply the oven forever. Wood-burning ovens do not contribute to the greenhouse effect because trees use up more carbon dioxide as they grow than the carbon dioxide produced when the wood is burnt.

Think about it!

1. **ABC** The packaging on Respect products help to sell them.
    a) Comment on how the use of colour, fonts and words sell this product.
    b) Can you think of a new name for an organic food producer? What message would you include on the packaging.
2. **PA** Carry out a comparison taste test comparing organic with non-organic fruit and vegetables. Can you tell which are organically grown?
3. Visit a supermarket to carry out some research and list the range of organic foods that are available.
4. **ICT** Use the Internet to find out more about the principles behind organic food or about one particular organic food producer. Write a report about it to read out to your class.
5. **ABC** Organic food is a 'value added' food. Explain what this means.
6. **ABC** Apart from wood, what other renewable energy sources are there?

Plenary

You have found out that there is more than one way of making bread commercially and that some food manufacturers consider nutritional, moral and ethical issues when making food products.

Designing bread

In the previous pages you have learned how to make bread and the functions of both its basic ingredients and any extra ingredients you can add to change its organoleptic properties. You have also found out how bread is mass-produced and how 'craft' bread is made. There are other criteria to consider when designing bread.

A

- Nutrition
- Equipment
- Occasion
- **Changing the properties of bread**
- Occasion
- Organoleptic properties
- Quality (mass or batch production)

Nutrition

Bread is a nutritious food. It is a starchy food that contains other vital nutrients. We are recommended to eat six slices of bread a day. Wholemeal flour can be used to increase the NSP (non-starch polysaccharide fibre) content of bread but this makes a dense loaf. A dense loaf is also produced if other grains, such as rye and corn, are used instead of wheat, because these grains contain very little gluten. People with coeliac disease can only eat bread made from other grains.

Adding extra ingredients to bread can improve the nutritional content of bread. Compare a basic white loaf with a stromboli loaf that has cheese and tomato added to it. Then look at the nutritional content of a pain au chocolat that has extra fat and chocolate added.

Bread for special occasions

Bread is an important part of many people's cultures. The Challah loaf is eaten on the Sabbath by Jews. Hot cross buns and harvest bread derive from Christian festivals. In Sweden, saffron bread is eaten at Christmas and Lucia Cats on 13th December.

B   *This is Prosphoro, traditionally used in the Greek Orthodox Eucharist service*

Special occasion bread can be more complicated to make than ordinary, everyday bread. Harvest bread is often made as a one-off loaf by a baker. Other breads would be made in small batches. If bread is mass-roduced it has to be easy and simple to make.

Think about it!

D What occasions or religious celebrations could you design bread for – Hallowe'en, Eid, Independence day? Make a mindmap of these special occasions and the types of bread that could be used for each.

Time

As you have learned, it takes time to make bread.

 **Quick bread**

If you are short of time, you could try a bread mix. A bread mix just needs warm water adding to it. You can buy a variety of mixes in most supermarkets. The one in **C** is for sun dried tomato and parmesan bread.

C   *A ready-made bread mix can save time*

Ready-made components

A bread mix is a **ready-made component**. Examples of other ready-made components are pizza bases, chopped dried herbs, grated cheese, ready-to-roll icing and cake mixes. The advantages of ready-made components are:

- they save time and reduce the skill needed by the cook, for example chopped herbs
- they reduce the need for equipment and space to store ingredients
- fewer workers are needed in food manufacturing where ready-made components, so costs are reduced
- they produce the same quality food product every time.

D   *There are many ready-made components available*

A pizza base will save the time of making the bread dough, waiting for it to prove and partly cook. There is no need to employ or train a worker to make bread and no need to buy a big mixer or proving cupboard. Pizza bases are stored in ambient temperatures so no fridges are needed to store fresh yeast. A bought pizza base will be the same quality every time whereas if the worker is not skilled, they could add too much salt by accident.

The disadvantages of ready-made components are:

- the component is more expensive than buying the raw ingredients. For example, a pizza base costs more than buying the flour, fat, salt and yeast.
- there are only a certain number of ready-made components available and they might not be the flavour or quality you want. For example, you might want a thin, garlic-flavoured pizza base but only be able to buy a thick, basic base.
- by using a component you rely on one supplier to provide that component. The supplier might decide to change the component to a different taste or shape. They might even decide to stop producing that component or may go out of business.

Think about it!

1   Look at the school canteen meal below. Work out how many ready-made components could be used to make this meal.

> Tomato soup with a bread roll
>
> Shepherds pie with carrots and sweetcorn
>
> Cherry pie and custard

2   **ABC** Think of a ready-made component like the ones in **D**.

   a) List its advantages and disadvantages.

   b) Explain who would most likely use this component.

   c) In what situation you would use this component yourself.

Plenary

There are several criteria you need to consider when you design bread.

HACCP

If you cook a dish for your family and it makes them ill, it is unpleasant but only a few people are affected. If a food factory cooks a batch of family-sized spaghetti bolognaise meals and 200 families became ill, it would be a health scandal.

The food industry has, by law, to be extremely careful when preparing food products for sale to make sure they are safe to eat. All food manufacturers use a system called **HACCP** (Hazard Analysis and Critical Control Point) to ensure food products are safe to consume. HACCP is part of quality assurance. Food manufacturers use this HACCP system to analyse

what *could* go wrong during production and establish controls to *stop* anything going wrong.

HACCP identifies hazards (see pages 50–1). A hazard is anything that can cause harm to a consumer. It can be biological (food poisoning bacteria), chemical (bleach) or physical (glass or metal). All possible hazards that can cause harm become critical control points because they must be stopped or avoided. These critical control points must be monitored regularly to make sure they do not become a hazard.

HACCP plans

A shows part of the HACCP plans for Golden West Foods. These HACCP plans do not have many critical control points because bread-making does not involve high risk-foods. A HACCP plan for a ready-prepared meal, such as a chicken curry, will have more critical control points.

You can see from the example that hazards are identified against the process and then controls put in place to stop the hazard happening. The controls are monitored (check that the controls are working).

Hazards can happen throughout the process. Table **B** shows all the steps of a process, the possible hazards that could occur and how they can be monitored.

 A   An extract from an HACCP plan for Golden West Food

Control point no & location (Critical Control Point No)	Potential hazards	Critical limits	Control, responsibility & frequency	Deviation procedure	Control records location	Monitoring, responsibility & frequency	Monitoring records location
(Critical Control Point 1) Bulk ingredient Receiving & storage	Physical contamination	Bulk materials free from foreign bodies	Bakery Store Operative to check CoA and condition of vehicle for every delivery	If there is any suspicion of contamination notify Shift Manager and QA	CoA's held in QA Office Incoming goods and vehicles inspection records held in Bakery Store	QA Manager to check records during traceability checks and hygiene audits	Deviations noted in minutes of daily meetings Hygiene audit reports held in QA Office
(Critical Control Point 2) Flour sifters	Physical contamination	Maximum 2mm sifter mesh diameter	Examination of sifter tailings by Brew Operative every 2 hours	If there is any suspicion of contamination notify Shift Manager and QA Quarantine all production from previous 2 hours	Sifter tailings check records held in QA Office	QA Manager to check records during traceability checks and hygiene audits	Deviations noted in minutes of daily meetings Hygiene audit reports held in QA Office
	Sifter intact	Metal sifters (will set off Me Dets) Examination of sifter integrity by engineers every week	If sifter is damaged notify Shift Manager and QA Quarantine all production from previous 2 hours	Sifter integrity check records held in engineering	Chief Engineer monitors all engineering checks and logs results on KPI board	PPM records held in Engineering Engineer KPI board held in Team Room

Process		Possible hazards	Monitoring steps
Purchase		High-risk foods contaminated with bacteria	◦ Use reputable supplier ◦ Specify temperature
Receive food		High-risk foods contaminated with bacteria	◦ Does it smell, look, feel right? ◦ Check temperature
Storage		Growth of food poisoning bacteria	◦ Check temperature of fridge ◦ Rotate stock ◦ Wrap and label
Preparation		Cross contamination of high-risk foods Growth of bacteria	◦ Wash hands ◦ Use clean equipment ◦ Separate raw and cooked foods
Cooking		Survival of food poisoning bacteria	◦ Cook centre to above 75°C
Cooling		Growth of bacteria Contamination with bacteria	◦ Cool quickly, chill quickly ◦ Chill quickly ◦ Keep away from raw food
Assembly of dish		Cross contamination Growth of bacteria Contamination with bacteria	◦ Wash hands ◦ Use clean equipment ◦ Keep away from raw foods
Storage		Growth of bacteria	◦ Chilled storage – check below 4°C
Transportation		Growth of bacteria	◦ Chilled storage – check below 4°C

B

Think about it!

1 **ABC** Find a recipe for chicken curry with rice.
   a) Write out the process as a flow chart.
   b) Identify any possible hazards – don't forget to start with the purchase of the ingredients.
   c) Work out the controls needed to stop these hazards happening. How will you monitor these controls?
2 **ABC** Write a HACCP plan for the batch production of your bread.

3 **ABC** Explain the difference between a control point and a critical control point

Plenary

If you use your knowledge of hygiene, hazards and quality controls which you have gained over the past three years, you should be able to write a HACCP plan for every food product you make.

Glossary

All-in-one sauce sauce made by cooking starch, liquid and fat together

Analyse look carefully at and find a way to solve a problem. When you analyse some work you have carried out, for example a research questionnaire, you work out what you have learned or found out from this work and how it well help you in the next stage of your work

Attribute profile (or star profile) a diagrammatic method of showing sensory analysis characteristics

Bacteria micro-organisms, some of which may be harmful and contaminate foods (pathogenic bacteria), and some of which are useful, such as those in yoghurts

Balanced diet the right amount of energy and nutrients to meet the needs of the body. The balanced plate is a graphical method of showing what a balanced diet should be

Batch production a specific quantity of one product is produced in a single production run

Batch to make a mixture stick together using another ingredient

Biodegradable able to break down safely and relatively quickly by biological means into natural raw materials and return to the environment

Bland tasteless

Bulk the main ingredient in a recipe

Coagulation the process by which a liquid turns to a solid as the protein sets

Component parts what a product is made from, for example, a pizza consists of a bread base, a tomato layer, cheese and often extra toppings

Consumers people who buy and use food products. They have a choice about the kind of food products they buy. Not all consumers want the same food products

Criteria rules or targets against which a product is checked

Design specification (criteria) information about what kind of product you should make

Designers people in the food industry who develop new food products

Diversity variety

Extruded forced through a die or a nozzle under pressure, for example, biscuit mixtures or potato snacks

Fermentation a biological process that occurs when gas and heat are produced by micro-organisms (bacteria or yeast) as they convert organic material into energy needed to multiply

Flowchart a chart showing the sequence of stages in the design and making of a food product

Functional properties characteristics of ingredients that can be used to produce particular types of mixtures and food products

Gelatinisation thickening process caused by heating a liquid and a starch

Genetically modified food biologically changed in some way, for example, to give a higher nutritional value in rice, to make plants more resistant to pests or to make animals grow faster

Glaze a smooth, shiny coating on food, usually made using milk, sugar or egg

HACCP (Hazard Analysis and Critical Control Point) a system for caterers and food manufacturers used to control food safety procedures

Hazard anything that has the potential to cause harm to the consumer

Hygiene cleanliness, keeping clean to prevent food poisoning

Imperial measurements in ounces, pounds, fluid ounces and pints

Input food, material or information at the start of a system

Manufacturing specification a more detailed production plan including every detail that a manufacturer needs to make a product again and again

Mass production the same product is produced in very large quantities

Metric measurements in grams, kilos, millilitres and litres

Modelling developing and trying out ideas either using a computer (nutritional modelling) or small qualities of actual ingredients (functional, sensory modelling)

Modified starch starch that has been developed chemically so that it forms a gel with cold water or milk

Nutrients components of foods that do particular jobs in the body. All food is made up of nutrients. Different foods contain different amounts and types. The main nutrients are carbohydrates, fats, proteins, vitamins and minerals. Our bodies need the right balance of nutrients each day

Nutritional profile using a computer programme to find the nutritional value of food products. This information is found on packaging to inform the consumer

One-off production one product is made at a time. It is likely to be a quality product and relatively expensive. This kind of product is often made for a special occasion, for example a celebration cake

Organic products produced without the use of chemical pesticides, fungicides or herbicides, without the use of fertilisers, growth regulators or stimulants that make crops or animals grow faster and without using unnecessary antibiotics or intensive farming methods

Organoleptic properties the qualities or properties of a food that can be described during sensory analysis (tasting). When we use our senses we can find out about a food's appearance, texture, aroma and flavour

Output the finished product or final result of a system

Pathogenic harmful

People profiles information about target consumers

Preservation treating food to make it last longer, for example by freezing, adding sugar or acid, or drying

Processed food food that has been changed in some way from its original state, for example, cheese, flour, tomatoes, corned beef and ready-prepared meals

Product analysis finding out about a food product by looking at it, reading the packaging, taking the product apart (disassembly) and tasting it

Product specification describes what a particular product should be like

Production the way food products are made. They can be produced in several ways: one-off production, batch production, mass production

Production line a moving conveyor belt often used to assemble products. It is a way of speeding up the manufacturing process. A production line is usually used in mass production, sometimes in batch production

Properties of ingredients characteristics, for example, function, the nutrients ingredients contain and their sensory properties (taste, texture, aroma and appearance)

Prototypes sample products used for trials and market research

Quality assurance ensuring that products are of good quality and are safe

Ranking test placing samples of food or drink in order of preference

Rating test giving products a score on a scale of 1 to 5

Ready-made component raw ingredients that have been processed in some way

Recyclable can be used again, usually refers to packaging

Roux sauce made from a basis of flour and fat, liquid is then added

Sauce a liquid or semi-solid accompaniment to a meal

Seasonal characteristic of or available during a particular season

Sensory analysis describing characteristics of a food product, including appearance, colour, texture, taste and aroma

Shelf-life the length of time a food product remains safe to eat and of good quality

Snack a food product that consists of a casing (outside) and filling (inside)

Specification exact details of what a product should be like. *See also* design specification, product specification, manufacturing specification

Standard product a product in everyday use

Staple foods the main part of a person's diet, usually grown in their home country and is a cheap, starchy food such as potatoes or rice

Starchy foods foods that provide energy, for example, bread, cereals and potatoes

Sterilised heat-treated to remove all micro-organisms

Sweated heated slowly in fat or butter

System the series of tasks needed to create a finished product, made up of inputs and outputs

Taste panel a group of people who taste food and drink and give views on characteristics, for example, taste and texture

Texture what food feels like in your mouth

Unit operation stages in the production process

Waxy maize starch starch that remains runny when cold

Index